(SIGNED)

To

Jam

Kindest regards

Ian Fraser

# Blood, Sweat, and Cheers

Ian Fraser

IAN FRASER

# Blood, Sweat, and Cheers

Illustrations by Ghislaine Howard

ISBN 0 7279 0246 6

The quotation from Louis MacNeice's poem "Carrickfergus" is reproduced from *Collected Poems of Louis MacNeice* by permission of Faber and Faber Ltd.

Printed in Great Britain by the
University Press, Cambridge

To Eleanor, Mary-Alice, and Mark, who have shared the burden of a busy life

# Contents

# Introduction

When I was asked by the editor of the *British Medical Journal* if I would be willing to write some personal reminiscences of my life as a surgeon over the past 60 years, I found myself in a slight dilemma. On the one side I felt that I would merely be telling the story of a provincial surgeon with more or less the same experiences that have been the lot of all surgeons of my age, a story well known to most people, and with possibly little original to tell. However, the past 60 years have produced the greatest advances in surgery since that piece of Anglo-French cooperation featuring Messrs Pasteur and Lister in the 1860s. In the 1880s von Bergmann from Berlin went a step further when, by the use of steam sterilisation, he suggested aseptic surgery – "Prevent the germ" – rather than the antiseptic surgery – "Kill the germ" – of Lister. Today von Bergmann's method forms the basis of modern surgery.

Surgery was made possible in the nineteenth century by the discovery of the three a's – anaesthesia, antisepsis, and asepsis – appearing in that order in the 1840s, the 1860s, and the 1880s, so it was left to this century to consolidate these achievements and open the door to today's modern advances. My personal 40 years in active surgery were divided almost equally into two parts, the first 20 years under pre-National Health Service conditions, the "bad old days." In my second 20 years I was very much the participant in the ever-changing face of state medicine. Many doctors today forget that, before the NHS, surgeons were entirely honorary and could make a livelihood only by charging the patients, at least those who could pay. It was a sort of Robin Hood existence. With only a limited amount of private practice, the young man was carefully watched and often had his wings clipped by his seniors who did not want to see any inroad made into their private practice and income, at times a meagre one. Today it is very different when we see the senior registrar in some areas with a larger income than the consultant.

Although we may speak with pride of the many advances that have been made, we are inclined to forget the trials and errors that took place before a final success was achieved. If at times we look back with some shame we must remember we were doing what was the accepted practice at that time. We all committed many sins – mostly sins of commission rather than of omission.

The same thing is happening today. What that wise man from Boston said some years ago is very true: "50% of the advances we are so proud of today will be discarded in ten years' time but sadly today we have not the knowledge to know which half to discard." If this applies to surgery it applies even more so to medicine. Almost weekly by post we get warning letters of the dangers and side effects of some drugs. I for one will indeed be glad when I see cortisone barred. I have always before me the unhappy memory of three very nice ladies, the wives of personal friends, all of whom had to have both legs amputated for gangrene due to cortisone given for some years for rheumatoid arthritis. A patient with both legs off and with hands virtually useless through rheumatoid arthritis rarely lives any length of time. This drug is only one of many that we all could think of. Like Ko-Ko in *The Mikado* many of us can say "I've got a little list" of those that never would be missed.

With all these things running through my head I felt it might be worth while to put them down on paper, and so I wrote to the editor to say that with his help I would have a go. Naturally what I write is a personal saga, but it applies with minor differences to all those young men of my period.

I have purposely written this mostly from memory, which means that there will be inexactitudes, and so for the mistakes and for the grey areas I beg some indulgence.

# Acknowledgments

I thank my secretary Joan Sayers for her skill in putting the indecipherable into impeccable print. Also I must thank Professor John Braidwood (professor of English), for although a Scot he was able to put this impeccable typescript into correct English, spelling, grammar, punctuation, etc; Ruth Holland who sorted out a series of short articles and made them into a readable almost continuous story, and, finally, Ghislaine Howard for her delightful illustrations.

Where would we be without the experts?

# Between the mountain and the gantries LOUIS MACNEICE

## GROWING UP IN BELFAST

*Father – the Puritans – school with the girls and in the
shadow of the Somme – medical school – the teachers and
the taught*

# Family matters

Of my own personal background there is nothing very important or worthy to report. My father was a single-handed general practitioner, so naturally I was brought up in a busy medical atmosphere. My maternal grandfather was also a general practitioner. Concerning my grandfather two incidents stand out. Firstly, he wrote in the 1860s a very good paper on caisson disease. He described in detail the state of men brought to the surface – perhaps too rapidly or perhaps too late – who had been working on the bed of the River Foyle in Londonderry where they were building up from below the pillars for the first stone bridge to cross that broad and fast-flowing river. His details of the men, some of whom did not survive, was a very good paper for a man in general practice, who must have been well in advance of his time. The other incident was a sad one. He and the district nurse were called out to see a case of typhus fever in a small house on the roadside. The doctor and the nurse both contracted the disease and both died, while the patient lived. This was not unusual. These patients often had developed a certain degree of immunity which the healthier people had not got. So my mother was deprived of her father when she was only six years old.

Speaking of my father I cannot say enough. He wrote with a very clear hand which he said he developed when he thought of joining the Indian Civil Service; this is one of his many genes which was not passed on to his son. He later considered going out to China as a missionary with the China Inland Mission. This idea, however, he abandoned when his only brother died, and he felt he must stay at home to look

3

after his elderly parents. At this stage he took up medicine, having already graduated with an arts degree. I always envied him his knowledge of Greek and Latin. To be able to sit in church, as he did, reading his Greek testament was given to very few. I owe everything to my father, a man who with a real working religion taught me, or at least tried to teach me, integrity and humanity. He was an interesting man, an enthusiast for anything that he took up. He had a splendid sense of humour, able to laugh at himself as well as at others.

My father was one of the earliest motorists in Belfast. His first car was a five-horse-power Vauxhall. It was probably at least fourth-hand when he got it. It had been brought to Belfast by two brothers called Chambers, engineers, who thought they would like to build a motor car. They brought several old ones of different makes from England, cannibalised them, and got the necessary ideas. They then rebuilt these cars and resold them. In actual fact they did produce a very good car, "The Chambers," still on view in our local museum, but sadly a small firm like that cannot compete with the large industrial giants. As a small boy I had to play my part helping to grind in valves on the kitchen floor, or repair punctures, which were very frequent in those days. The tyres were poor and the horses were many.

Another personal matter that I should mention was that my mother died within two years of my birth. She had developed phthisis early on in her pregnancy and so my father was left, a sad and lonely man for some years, with the problem of a small and only child on his hands. My paternal grandfather was a civil servant, and with a name like Fraser came, naturally, from the Highlands of Scotland. On my mother's death I went back from time to time to live with my grandparents. They were very kind but it was a very strict Puritan household which even as a small boy I found rather overpowering. We were the only house in that particular area where the blinds were kept down on Sunday, something hard to realise today.

I must say, however, that my father married very happily some five or six years later and he and my second mother –

4

she became to me my mother – had a very happy married life together for some 40 years. No one was brought up in a happier home, and I cannot be grateful enough.

Talking of cars, although my father had a series of old ones, mostly second and third hand, he always kept his bicycle, his first love, which he rode almost to the end of his life. I remember when he got his first Ford, Model "T". On swinging it one morning to make it start, he got the well known backfire and sustained a "chauffeur's fracture" of the wrist. This is a fracture that no longer exists – no one would think today of cranking his motor car, in fact no car has a starting handle. Today when the battery fails you just have to push the car, and so now you get a cardiac arrest rather than a fractured wrist. (Of course the chauffeur himself is now getting rarer and will soon be an endangered species.) During the first world war, for national economy, my father bought two motor bicycles and sidecars, one for himself and one for me. I was very glad to have my Douglas motor bicycle and sidecar when I went to university and later still when I was a house surgeon.

My father was a lover of books. Often when visiting a patient it was said that he looked at the books on the shelves and occasionally had to be called to order by a plaintive voice from the bed clothes suggesting that the patient would like to be looked at also.

I went as a day boy to the local grammar school, an old school with a good reputation; in fact my father had been to the same school as a boy and as a matter of medical interest in his form at school at the same time was a man who was to become famous later on – Almroth Wright.

Before going to my grammar school I had been at the local girls' school for about five years, so it was quite a shock when I was thrown in at the deep end to the large day school of some 700 boys. By and large I enjoyed my school days. I took part in most of the school activities; the school plays, the OTC etc. At the OTC I became proficient in sending messages by semaphore and morse code, as a result of which I wore two crossed flags on my sleeve. I also learnt how to put on puttees. This required skill; if too loose they fall off, which on a route march produces total ignominy, but if too tight it produces gangrene, or at least it felt like that.

My school years coincided with the first world war. Life was austere, with food rationing and so on. Every Friday the head boy read out a letter from the headmaster which gave us the sad list of the old boys of the school who had been killed. We all stood up on this solemn occasion. As a sentimental youth I was always greatly impressed, as it contained so often the names of some of my heroes. We were a keen rugby-playing school and so often the name was one I had admired, perhaps a boy I had seen scoring a spectacular try or displaying some other piece of brilliant gamesmanship. I still remember well the deaths of many of the senior boys I had known at the school when the Ulster Division was decimated at the Battle of the Somme.

# Living and learning

I went up to the university in 1918, coinciding with the returning ex-servicemen from the first world war. This meant that my year at the university, as happened everywhere else, was a very large one.

In my preclinical years I felt I was a very ordinary student, but when I came to meet people and to "walk the wards" I felt much happier. My year was a very keen and hardworking one, ending up with 13 out of 120 candidates graduating with honours. Later, when it came to applying for house surgeon posts, there were 13 vacancies in our own teaching hospital. However, the Board of Management, quite rightly, gave all these posts to the ex-servicemen although in fact they all had only pass degrees. This meant that the younger men had all to find hospital posts elsewhere rather than in their own teaching hospital. I personally was fortunate in that one of the ex-servicemen – a man with a leg off, and married – decided that he must get into general practice at once as he could not afford a job at £50 per year.

As residents, we were very much the products of the war. Our teachers, senior and junior, had for the most part served in France. We were told regularly of the marvellous combined clinical meetings at the base in France which involved the cream of American, British, and French consultants. We were trying out the methods that had been invented in the war. Septic wounds were irrigated with small tubes inserted deeply into the wound and a continuous stream of Carrel Dakin fluid was kept running. Blood transfusion was still very primitive. Several methods had been tried. The first of these was the Kimpton tube. In this the blood was retained in a glass funnel which had been treated and made frictionless, rather like the non-stick pan of today. Another was the Bazett-Fullerton tube. This method consisted of joining up, with a small connecting tube, the donor's artery and the recipient's vein. The donor's heart did the pumping. The only disadvantage was that there was no way of measuring the amount, so we went on until the donor began to look pale and the recipient pink – not a very scientific method. It was of interest to us that Fullerton became professor of surgery in Belfast; I became his personal assistant for many years. Bazett did much of his work in Canada.

The first transfusion method used was the citrate method, and although it was the first to be used, it did not become popular; but actually it is today the basis of our modern blood transfusion service. The one in general use in our hospital was the defibrinated blood method. The blood from the donor was run into a flask, and through the cork of the flask was a glass rod with small spikes on it. As the flask was rotated the fibrin was deposited on this glass rod as a yellow spindle. The blood was now defibrinated and could no longer clot, and with no additives it caused of course no reaction. It was ideal, but difficult and tedious. To save man hours we used to put the flask on top of the turntable of a gramophone at the bedside so that the flask could be gently rotated.

In retrospect, blood transfusion was slow in being perfected when we think that this was the method in 1923 and yet the blood groups, the main problem, had been discovered nearly 22 years earlier. In fact we owe much to the Spanish civil war of 1936–9 for its ideas. It was partly from this that Sir Lionel Whitby built our own wartime blood transfusion service at Bristol, but even that had to be modified when the surgeons in the Eighth Army pointed out that plasma, although good for resuscitation, did not supply all the body wants. It was from that date that whole blood became the fundamental basis of our today's blood service. Plasma was handy, it did not need typing, it could be dried, and like dried milk it could be reconverted into a liquid again, but it had its limitations.

The contacts made in France by our chiefs had also many advantages as we got many illustrious visitors whom we otherwise would not have had. I remember Harvey Cushing giving a very good lecture. Percy Sergeant came and was good enough to operate, something that many people did not like to do except on their own pitch. Ernest Myles did a rectal resection. Hugh Hampton Young from Baltimore described his operation for prostatectomy using the perineal route. It was a great day when the Mayo Brothers (Dr Charlie and Dr Will) paid us a visit. The university in most cases was most cooperative and willing to give an honorary degree if they considered our visitors were of sufficient merit. This all meant a great deal to men of my period. Today, having got his FRCS, I am told the budding surgeon must get his BTA (been to America). None of us got to America and so it was really a case of the mountain coming to Mohammed.

In those days for operating we mostly wore our outdoor clothes. We did change into white theatre boots and take off our ties, but it was mostly done in trousers and braces with a sterile gown covering this all up. The first time that white shirt and trousers appeared was after Fullerton had paid a visit to the Mayo Clinic; in fact when he appeared for the first time on the hospital corridor suitably attired one of his colleagues is said to have remarked, "Off to play tennis, I see." What a change today with barrier nursing and red lines and double red lines all over the place. Some years ago a colleague of mine did an interesting test. He had a swab taken from the sole of his outdoor shoes as he entered the hospital one morning, having walked some 50 to 100 yards from the car park. Later, on leaving the hospital in the afternoon, having spent the day in the wards and outpatient department, he had a further swab taken. The report was, as one would expect, that the shoes were safer on entering the hospital than they were on leaving.

Almost in my first week as a house physician I was faced with a problem. A middle-aged man was admitted at 7 30 am straight from the Liverpool boat with a severe lung haemorrhage. I saw him on arrival in the ward. He asked the nurse to leave the room as he wished to speak to me privately.

He then told me that he knew he had advanced tuberculosis of the lungs. He had had a similar haemorrhage before and in fact had been told by his doctor that he had only some months to live. He then asked me to give him a large dose of morphia so that he could slip away quietly. He pointed out to me that I was a well trained doctor who knew the answers, and also that if I had any feelings of sympathy and humanity it was my duty to help him. He then went on to say it was his wish to go and the only third person involved was God. From what he knew of God he thought that he was a kind god who would understand what we were going to do. As a very young man I had never had this problem put up to me before by a senior, well educated man. Fortunately, I was able to stall and "kick for touch," and he eventually went back to England and I am sure did die some months later.

I never had the same request put up to me again. On one occasion, however, I had to stop a doctor giving his sister a fatal injection of morphia. She was my patient and dying from a cancer of the breast with many secondaries. Had he done this without my knowledge I could not have objected, but when he asked the matron of the nursing home to have a syringe filled for him when he called back later I had to intervene. I could not let the matron or myself be fellow conspirators.

Syphilis was fairly common and did appear at times in the general surgical wards. It was treated with "914" (neo-salvarsan). In 1912 "606" (salvarsan) had been replaced with neosalvarsan, Erhlich having carried out a further 300 experiments to simplify the treatment. It was still a large, troublesome intravenous injection, and a very toxic one if it escaped into the tissues. It was, however, the first stage in chemotherapy. It is hard to believe that there was all that trouble when syphilis can be cured today with such ease and comfort.

When I was a house physician we had in the ward on one occasion a case of GPI (general paralysis of the insane). A new treatment had just been suggested and that was to give the patient malaria. The theory for this arose from the fact that a troopship bringing servicemen back on the long journey from the Far East had a few GPI patients among the personnel. It was found that some of these patients who suffered malaria on the passage home had apparently been cured, or had certainly had their symptoms greatly reduced. There seemed to be no scientific basis for this. Perhaps it was the hyperthermia that it produced. It was very much advocated by a senior physician in Harley Street (incidentally, a graduate of my own university).

When this patient came into the ward I was asked by my chief to take him to another hospital where there was a known case of malaria, so when the malarial patient was at the height of his fever I took my patient in my motor bicycle and sidecar and transferred 10 cc of the infected blood from the malarial patient and brought the GPI patient back. As expected he shot a high temperature a few days later, but suddenly and sadly he died, so I had 100% mortality rate with my series of one case.

Talking of my motor bicycle, I used this every Saturday to go to play hockey. I had given up rugby because, being small, I got a good many injuries from the marauding forwards who had no finer feelings, I found, for the chap at the base of the scrum; with a hockey stick I had at least some method of self defence. On this particular Saturday I left the hospital at 1 pm to go to a match in the country. On my way down from the hospital a small girl of 10 or so ran out in front of me, and I knocked her down. To my delight she began to yell and ran off, but unfortunately this took place just outside a pub with many not very friendly semi-alcoholics looking on.

I was soon surrounded by a small crowd of rather unfriendly faces. I heard one man say, "I saw you coming down like the hammers of Hell." It was something in fact which my Douglas bicycle at its best could never have done. Things were very unpleasant, and finally an enormous man, more alcoholic than the rest, appeared and forced his way into the centre of the crowd. I felt exactly as they must have done in the French Revolution as they mounted the steps for the guillotine. This man came forward – and then in a very loud voice said, "I never saw better driving; many men would have killed that girl."

The crowd no longer took any interest and walked away. I then spoke to my friend and told him how much I appreciated his help. He then went on to tell me that he had not seen the incident at all, he had been still in the pub, but when he came out he recognised me as the man who was looking after his "missus" in the hospital. He said, "You have given her b – good treatment." I rapidly assured him that if she had had good treatment up to date it was nothing to what she was going to get from now on.

I think as students we did more in the side room to the wards than is done now. Today it seems to be chiefly a cafeteria – nothing wrong with that. In my day boiling of urine for albumin was a daily chore. Today a small dipstick like a miniature totem pole gives the answer. We spent a long time each day boiling up Feiling's solution to see how the diabetic patients were doing, and of course every gastric case had to have a test meal. The patient swallowed the gruel of porridge and later, through a Ryle's tube, specimens were withdrawn every half hour. This total process could go on for up to two hours or more, in fact until the stomach was empty. The final graph when the acid was titrated gave very valuable information of the gastric acidity. I was told that a high-powered senior physician was recently taken to see a patient in a surgical ward. He asked to see the lab reports on the blood chemistry. He made up a suitable cocktail changing the various blood salts, etc, and when asked to see the patient he said that was not necessary. He does not yet know whether the patient was an elderly prostatic gentleman or a charming teenager. He may be right, but surely he has lost something.

When I was a house surgeon in the gynaecological wards I had on occasions to do an interesting job for the professor of gynaecology. He was a man interested at that time in treating cancer of the womb with a radon tube – a tube smaller than one's fifth finger. This was obtained from the Radium Institute in London; the tube was delivered to the guard at Euston for the train to Liverpool; then by some means it was given to the captain of the Liverpool-Belfast boat to be collected at the quay in Belfast next morning as soon as the boat arrived. This is where I came in. My job was to meet the boat, collect the little box, and speed with it on my motor bicycle to a certain nursing home where the patient would be already on the table and fully anaesthetised. Timing was important. I had to ring up the docks to see that the boat was not delayed by fog, get as correct an estimated time of arrival as possible, and then inform the nursing home. In retrospect it was all such nonsense when we think that this tube lost 50% of its value in the first 24 hours, most of it on the train and boat, leaving what was left a very weak dose of radiation. Today with air flights things would be much easier but much less exciting.

In my time as a resident two valuable discoveries were made. The first of these was insulin. I remember vividly the clinical pathologist to the hospital demonstrating it on the polished floor of the board room: some six or eight rabbits were released to hop along the floor. After a time they were given insulin and all collapsed. Later they were given an injection of glucose and slowly recovered to amble off still, I am afraid, with a truly alcoholic gait.

The clinical pathologist is an extinct appointment now. He was a very popular consultant with general practitioners because he saw the patient, gave a clinical opinion, and took masses of specimens for testing, and the practitioner was informed as soon as possible. He was very unpopular with the rigid consultant physicians who gave a clinical opinion, perhaps carried a thermometer, a stethoscope, and a blood pressure apparatus, but had to get another person to deal with any test they took. They for their part said that the clinical pathologist, taking specimens from every orifice of the body, was doing a lot of unnecessary work. The clinical pathologist was not popular in the lab either, as he often occupied much time and material there with his private cases, often working until the small hours.

The other discovery that I still remember well was the suggestion of treating pernicious anaemia with raw liver. I remember a particular patient, a middle-aged man from the country, who had been in and out of hospital for a few years. A blood transfusion was given at regular intervals. Finally it was decided that this could go on no longer, and I was told to explain to his wife that we had nothing more to offer. However, on the Sunday before he was due to go home I read in that week's *British Medical Journal* that if we gave raw liver we might achieve some sort of success. I had a very cooperative ward sister. We got the necessary liver, ground it up into a horrible mess, added HP sauce, put it into a red or green tumbler so that the patient could not see how horrible it was – and it did the trick. After several weeks that patient went home and was kept well until more highly developed treatment came on the market.

I always think that that simple story of Minot's is so interesting. Having made the discovery of liver treatment, Minot wrote to all his old pernicious anaemia patients to come along to see him. There was the expected response that they had all died. But then one old lady whom he had seen 10 years before turned up, miserable and scraggy but living. He said he knew she had been eating liver; she denied this, but they then went over her diet. She finally admitted that she had one weakness which she could rarely afford, but perhaps once every one or two months in the year she would buy a pot of pâté de foie gras. This small spark was all that was needed to keep her red cells going, a further proof of his theory if even that was necessary.

There were two grades of consultant in my day: the visiting honorary surgeon in charge of beds, and an assistant surgeon who did outpatient clinics only and had no official beds of his own. Often the assistant was attached to a senior for whom he did the emergency work and often in return he was allowed to have a few beds, perhaps four, in his own name. This meant nothing because many of the other beds in the ward held patients whom the assistant had dealt with in the middle of the night, perhaps for a strangulated hernia, an acute appendix, a perforated duodenal ulcer, and suchlike. This system was a very bad one. Often in the outpatient department the assistant surgeon would see a patient and discuss and suggest treatment, but when the patient was admitted to the ward he saw someone else, who often suggested an entirely different type of treatment. The assistant surgeon, doing so many outpatient clinics, made many contacts with the family doctors and therefore built up quite a large consulting practice, but with only four personal beds he had no place to put the patients referred to him.

There were many nursing homes where patients could be admitted cheaply, but the shortage of personal beds meant that quite a large amount of surgery was done in the patient's own home. As a house surgeon, and later as a registrar, I used to be taken out on many of these trips. It was often to the country and often at night. My job as the junior member was to be the handyman, a sort of jack of all trades. I might be asked to drive the car, often on the way back when my senior wanted a snooze. At the operation I might assist, or give the anaesthetic. This depended on what the general practitioner wanted to do or did not want to do. At the house itself I had to set the scene while my chief was upstairs seeing the patient, and I was responsible for getting the room suitably arranged down below – taking the flowers off the piano, making a good open space for the kitchen table; one did not do too much disturbing of furniture as this raised the dust, and there was usually a good deal of it available as the place had not been dusted for ages, if ever. I had to make sure there was a free access to hand basins. From all this I learnt a lot, and so when my time came to do this type of surgery I found it not too difficult. (I have happy memories of operating on a strangulated hernia in a cottage close to the water's edge in a small seaside village. There was a knock at the window and I found it was an inquisitive hen wondering what was going on.)

Domiciliary surgery has now gone out. I was quite astonished to see that George VI had both his operations as domiciliary surgery – his lumbar sympathectomy and later his partial lobectomy. However, my colleagues and I had not the facilities of Buckingham Palace with its suction, skyalytic light and all other amenities laid on. It was all a very good training, and I suppose it helped me somewhat when later, in the second world war, I had to improvise again.

One of the features of my year at the university was a wonderful concert party or pierrot group that we had. They

were quite outstanding and were asked to perform all over
the province. At that time it was considered by many to be a
sign of an ill-spent youth, but looking back now I see that one
member became a professor of anatomy, another a professor
of pathology, another became a member of parliament,
another a senior psychiatrist in New York and another an air
vice-marshal. This all goes to prove that you can work hard
and play hard and thus get the most out of life. Some can do
only one, but the sad chap is the one who does neither.

# Under instructions

I always thought that teaching was one of the most important parts of the life of a hospital consultant. It was his duty to pass on all that he knew, and if his students did not end up better than he was then the teacher had failed. When I went up to university many of the teachers either died or retired. I must point out that there was no connection between these two events. The deaths were from natural causes and the retirements were due to the fact that many people had been kept on after retirement age as no appointments were to be made during the war "till the boys come home."

The professor of gynaecology had just died. He had had an interesting habit of always showing off at his lectures in the afternoon the proceeds of his morning's work, like a fisherman exhibiting his "catch." His bag was left by his chauffeur in the lecture room before the lecture, and so it was there when he arrived. This all came to an end when on one occasion, after he had given a dramatic account of the largest ovarian cyst that he had ever removed – almost like Gracie Fields's "biggest aspidistra in the world" – with everyone now ready, he opened the bag and produced to his astonishment two very dirty football boots which one of the students had put in, having removed the ovarian cyst. It was all taken in good part as actually the professor's own son was playing rugby for Ireland on the wing at that time, but although he continued to bring the bag to the lecture, from now on he always brought it in himself.

His successor had a brilliant brain but was not very interested in teaching. He held the theory that neither the cerebral cortex nor the gluteus maximus could stand – or sit

– a lecture of more than 40 minutes. This suited him and the students. He operated rapidly and skilfully with less instruments than I have ever seen anyone use before or since, perhaps three or four artery forceps. On one occasion some Americans came into the theatre and they were heard to say, "Professor, you sure go light on the hardware." His colleague was the reverse – meticulous, occasionally wearing two pairs of rubber gloves. His lecture lasted the full 60 minutes, and with seven or eight headings was the students' delight as they were able to put it all down on paper.

In surgery the senior professor retired as I arrived. He had been in the chair for 32 years, so his lectures had become somewhat fossilised. He often wore spats and always a white lining to his waistcoat, and as he talked at the bedside he kept the fob on his watch chain spinning round all the time. Before an operation he always sat down with his eyes closed for a short time. We never knew whether he was saying a quick prayer or revising his anatomy, or perhaps just having a short snooze. Once into action, however, he did a magnificent job. Although to me he looked a very old man, and frail, after he retired he lived for another 17 years and even represented the university as a member of parliament at Westminster. He had been a consultant surgeon in France, having been appointed by the Royal College of Surgeons of England. In the first world war names for consultant posts in the RAMC were put forward by the three royal colleges. One of the stories that he often told was of when he did a post-mortem on the famous former German airman Richtofen, the "Red Baron." The British claimed that he had been shot down in aerial combat, but the Germans insisted that he had made a forced landing behind the British lines and that we had actually shot him as he sat in the cockpit of his plane. The post-mortem proved conclusively that he had been shot in the air, but two years ago I read in a German paper that this was still denied.

The professor was very long-winded at times. I remember one day when dealing with a large abscess he said, "This will require tincture of iron in the surgical sense." He meant a good cut with the scalpel. (This phrase can only be understood now when we remember that tinct ferri perchlor was then in daily use for almost all forms of infection.) His successor was a different type, a man who tried to keep up with modern advances. He had an original mind and was a pioneer in urology, being one of the first to popularise the cystoscope. He had difficulty on one occasion in trying to impress a colleague. He brought him into the theatre and told him he would let him see the inside of the bladder and show him a vein or an artery. Finally, having found one he said, "Ah come here, I see a vessel," to which it is said that his rather cynical colleague replied, "Is it my duty now to say 'Ship ahoy'?"

The professor of medicine was a small man and a bachelor. He gave detailed lectures but was rigid in that he must have the correct words in any answer. A cardiac murmur must be "rough, rumbling and ingravescent," whatever that means. He wrote a small book which we had to know almost off by heart. In a case of pneumonia he insisted that the patient "lies like a log in bed." At one examination the candidate was asked, "How does the patient with pneumonia lie in bed?"

The candidate answered, "Still, motionless, etc, etc."

"No," said the professor, "the patient lies like a log in bed," to which it is said the candidate replied, "I have never seen a log in bed."

It was interesting to see the idiosyncrasies of our various teachers. One man wrote all his notes in shorthand so that his assistant could not read them. The assistant promptly took a course in shorthand but when it was complete he found it was the wrong type of shorthand, so he had to start all over again – very annoying. One of our teachers made a vast amount of money from his books, especially one called *Dictionary of Treatment*. It had no originality but was a compilation: it gave perhaps the 31 causes of diarrhoea, the 23 causes of vomiting, the 19 causes of headache, and so on. It was bought by the British Merchant Navy and it became compulsory on any seagoing ship that did not carry a doctor for the captain to have this at his bedside next to the Bible. It was translated into many languages, including Chinese. It brought him a lot of money. As he had no children the hospital, the university, and other charities all benefited from it.

He was an interesting man; his daily reading was the Book of Daniel and the stock market, so he kept a foot in both worlds. He loved to dress up, and as a deputy lieutenant he was entitled to wear knee breeches and the other garments that went with that appointment. This he did on suitable occasions. His wife, on the other hand, was interested in the Salvation Army. They must have looked a rather incongruous couple when, at a garden party at Buckingham Palace, he went wearing his deputy lieutenant's uniform and she in full dress Salvation Army kit.

One of our surgical consultants had been trained for a time at The Hospital for Sick Children in Great Ormond Street and when he came back to Belfast, although now a general surgeon, he continued to dissect out tonsils using the Denis Browne technique. He got a great reputation for this and quite rightly. This was, however, resented by the ENT fraternity, who objected to an inroad into their domain. I may say that most of them at that time were still using the guillotine method, which at times avulsed the tonsil but at other times just decapitated it. The matter came to a head when one of the ENT surgeons approached the chairman of staff of the hospital to lodge an official complaint. In that year the chairman of the staff was the senior gynaecologist. When he was approached about the problem he took the ENT surgeon aside and explained to him that the body had five orifices, that the ENT department had collared three of these, leaving one each for the gynaecologist and the surgeon, and that he did not feel any great sympathy if the general surgeon did make an occasional sally into the ENT department.

Every school has its eccentrics and ours was certainly no exception. An eccentric is an interesting chap. He is loved by the students because he is often anti-establishment – in fact often the official opposition – but he is rarely popular with his colleagues. He is a stimulating teacher because he often disagrees with the textbook. He perhaps excites the young student more than the older man, but later they find that he does not help in the easy running of the hospital.

The particular man I am thinking of was the senior surgeon for many years; a personality – a loner to a certain extent, but this was self-inflicted. On one occasion he sent an article to the *British Medical Journal* and when they declined to print it he resigned from the British Medical Association. He went up for his FRCS; they had the affrontery to fail him, so he never went up again. He had many interesting theories. Infection at that time was not curable, so indeed anyone was entitled to chose his own method. The surgeon in question thought that serum was the answer so he went regularly to the abattoir, collected the blood, extracted the serum, and had this given to his patients. He preferred "old cow" serum because the old cow had lived longer and therefore must have produced a serum with greater resistance. This serum was a very unpleasant drink, so he conceived the idea of drying it and converting it into powder or tablets which could be spread on bread like a sandwich. As his house surgeon for a short time I have had to drink it and eat it, and I can say that it has done me no harm – so far.

With sepsis so frequent it was this surgeon's custom to fill a large wound with urea crystals before closing it. There was also a large drain left; as the urea was very hygroscopic it produced a large discharge. The idea was that this cleansed the wound. I never saw this used anywhere else except that some ENT surgeons used to put it into a discharging ear. The urea came in small sealed bottles, 12 or so to the box. On one occasion, in a patient who had had a total mastectomy, several months after the operation there appeared along the scar many nodules. These were thought, naturally, to be secondary recurrences. However, when one or two were removed they were found to contain broken glass. It turned out that the theatre sister, obviously of Scottish extraction, had found a broken bottle of urea, and being of a saving type she had put the urea and broken pieces of glass back into another bottle.

Personality can be a two-edged sword. It was said of Winston Churchill that no one could grow up around him, like a large pine tree in the forest which almost sterilises the ground around it. Attlee, on the other hand, was less important and less spectacular. He may have allowed other men to grow and for a time perhaps give a greater strength to his own particular party. The same applies in surgery. We can think of some great men who have produced a series of assistants who have gone far, but we can also think of some personalities who rather chased away the young man or at best did not give him the help that the young man required.

To teach undergraduates is most rewarding. You are dealing with virgin soil and a very receptive audience. You are teaching more than clinical medicine, you are teaching them etiquette, good manners, kindness, and a way of life. There is admittedly an examination at the end but that is not the immediate object. A good teacher is an extravert and a bit of a showman; he is not always the best surgeon. When I was a student for a short time at The London Hospital I remember so well one man whom we all greatly admired. He was always known as London's best teacher and worst surgeon. I was terrified of him in the class, but he examined me at the final FRCS and I found he was then a really helpful gentleman. I suppose we feel that about all examiners when we get through, the reverse when we fail.

All schools have their good teachers. I never saw the famous London neurologist who each day when he came to lecture walked into the theatre with a different gait. One day he came with a limp like poliomyelitis, another day with an arthritis of the hip, another day he had tabes, another day spastic diplegia, another a cerebellar tumour, another hysteria, etc, etc. The diagnosis had to be made by the class before the lecture started. Naturally his classes were full to the brim.

I always think that undergraduate teaching is best performed by the general surgeon who is in the day-to-day hurly-burly of a busy practice. It is only a man of that sort who can tell students what to do on a domiciliary visit. He can explain the difficulty of doing a rectal examination on a fat patient in the depth of a feather bed, and he can explain the acrobatics necessary to avoid being engulfed in the depth of this bed together with the patient. No full time professor of surgery ever had that exciting experience. For him the patient is sitting ready for the examination, teed up like a golf ball on the first tee.

Postgraduate teaching, on the other hand, is entirely different. The candidate thinks he knows his etiquette, good manners, and patient care; in fact he thinks he knows everything, and now all he wants is to pass another higher examination. There was one man in London who gave a very well attended grind and used to fill his pockets to overflowing with £5 or £10 notes, but he would quite honestly say, "I am not teaching you medicine but I promise that I will make you fit to get the MRCP." It was from many of these grinds that students' textbooks later were often produced. To teach is like the quality of mercy, "it blesseth him that gives and him that takes." One always remembers the various witticisms. I remember in London one teacher describing when and how to pass a urethral dilator after cutting a urethral stricture. I remember his instructions were to do it once a day for a week, once a week for a month, once a month for a year, and then after that every year on his birthday. I remember McNeill Love saying that 50 years ago.

The old "who was Coudé?" story is a well worn chestnut, but it now is no longer asked. It originated in the time of the gum elastic catheter which at that time was produced in three shapes, a pointed one, another with one angle, Coudé (French for elbow) and a third one, "Bi-Coudé." This one had two elbows to allow it to get into the bladder in cases of enlarged prostate. A common question to test the candidate was for the examiner to ask him, "Who was Coudé?" to which the bright boy taking a chance usually replied, "A famous French surgeon, Sir," which of course was what the examiner hoped would happen. This question was then always followed up by the next question, "Then who was Bi-Coudé?" The appropriate answer was said to be "His half brother, Sir." The old story had a wonderful boost some years ago when some Welshmen with a really good sense of humour wrote the whole story of "Professor Coudé" and his unit in a medical journal. They showed him operating, they showed his family, his hospital, his background, his published works – all very convincing. It was quoted by a very famous London surgeon in the next edition of his *International Textbook on Surgery*. He had swallowed the story hook, line, and sinker. He had, with some blushes, to make a correction and retraction some time later – it was indeed a wonderful leg-pull.

Sometimes the grinder was not very popular with his colleagues. On one of my very first meetings of the Association of Surgeons I sat beside an elderly surgeon. I was very young and I was totally ignored. A London surgeon, well known for his international textbook, got up to speak and I was quite excited to hear this man whom I had never seen. Suddenly the elderly gentleman beside me turned round and in a loud voice asked who I was and where I came from. I was horrified and let him see that I thought it sacrilege as this man on the platform was almost next to God as far as I was concerned. But it was no good, the elderly gentleman continued to talk, and finally said to me, "Surely you do not want to listen to that rubbish." Some years later I found that my elderly gentleman was right.

Talking of "next to God" reminds me of the story of a lady who was in a certain London hospital. She came home after two weeks, having had a very satisfactory operation, but she never saw the great man whose name was on the chart above her bed. She finally decided that she would go and see him in Harley Street. She told him how pleased she was to see him and how satisfied she was with her treatment, but she did think it queer that she had never seen the surgeon himself. The great man then said to her, "Do you go to church, and if so do you expect to see God?"

I saw the God complex on another occasion at a meeting abroad. The speaker was the great chest surgeon Sauerbruch. On the table on the platform where he was speaking was a warning light of red, yellow, and green. After the yellow light appeared he took no notice, and when he ignored the red light his audience began to stamp their feet. The chairman then got the red light to flash on and off, but Sauerbruch still continued as the stamping of the feet got louder. Finally Sauerbruch walked over to the light and with a sweep of his hand swept the whole apparatus on to the floor, remarking at the same time, "There is no connection between science and time." Rumour has it that he later died of general paralysis of the insane and that the delusions of grandeur were just then starting.

I remember a very special lecture on shock. It was an Arris and Gale lecture at the Royal College of Surgeons in London. It had the usual small attendance and was given by the senior surgeon at St Mary's Hospital. He described a case in great detail, saying he had finished his morning work at the hospital and had just walked down the steps, flanked by his house surgeon and registrar. The registrar was about to open the back door of his car, when the house surgeon would neatly put the rug over his knees. Just then on the footpath a middle-aged man suddenly collapsed in front of them. They bent down and they heard him say, "The doctors always told me my b – ulcer would burst some time." In fact they were witnessing a perforated duodenal ulcer in its very earliest stages. No one could have seen it sooner. It must be operated on at once before there was much peritoneal soiling. They got a porter, a stretcher, a trolley, the man was admitted, a quick premedication, a quick short back and sides to the pubic region, and the patient was on the table in 15 minutes. The operation went very well and the patient died. He was already shocked and they had given him no time for this to be dealt with before inflicting another insult. It was a dramatic case and well told, and certainly accentuated a very important principle. I repeated this story over and over again for 10 years or so, telling my students about it every time we had a perforated ulcer in the ward. Finally one day I ran into Zachary Cope and said I must thank him as I had used his story so often and with such success.

"Yes," he said "it was a good story; of course you know it never did happen, I made it up the night before."

I really was shaken. I did not know whether to laugh or be annoyed with myself or him.

I remember the professor of medicine in Belfast telling me that he took a quick grind for his MRCP in London and was told of the examiners' idiosyncrasies. To percuss a chest one examiner liked you to hit the chest with a thump like a navvy hitting a London pavement, while another expected you just to touch it and make it ring like a wine glass. He was horrified to find that for this examination these two men had been paired together. So he had great difficulty in deciding what to do.

I gave a grind for many years to the final year medical students and got a great deal of fun from it, and a little money; very little. Later I was asked occasionally to help someone wanting a higher degree. One GP, in a very busy practice in the country, said he wished to try for his final FRCSI. He had got the primary part some 40 years earlier as a student. He was now over 60. He said he wanted the degree really to put on his tombstone. He came to see me for some time rather late on a Thursday afternoon, his day off. He invariably fell asleep. Sleep is very infectious and eventually I found that I was doing the same, and I am not sure which of us woke up first. However, to make a long story short, he did go up for the examination and got it; I presume he put the examiners to sleep. He did eventually put the FRCSI on his tombstone, but he also put it on his brass plate the day after the results came out.

I gave a grind to an old student who had moved into the Republic of Ireland and had to get a higher surgical degree to keep the surgical appointment at the local hospital. He was not able to get the FRCS but an MCh would be adequate. After he was successful we became great friends. He was a much respected man in his own area and he became quite a politician. Late one night he rang me up asking me to go at once over the border as he had a problem that he could not discuss on the telephone, so at midnight with my registrar, for fear I broke down and had a puncture, I travelled 150 miles to keep the appointment. I found that the surgeon had operated on the local member of parliament for that area. He had found that the patient had an advanced and hopeless abdominal cancer and was certainly going to die. The problem was that the MP was of a different political party to the surgeon, and the surgeon had decided that on the death of the patient he would go up for the by-election when it took place, and he felt that I, of a different persuasion politically and otherwise, should at least take part of the responsibility, as it might not look too good for him to kill the sitting member and then go up for his seat. In fact all this did happen; he did go up for the election, but was beaten by the deceased's son. I suppose it is really best to keep medicine and politics apart.

I remember that visit vividly. We went back at 4 am to have bacon and eggs with the surgeon's wife before going home. Before I left he asked if I liked venison. I was able to say truthfully that I got very little of it. He said he did not like it but there had been a "shoot" a few days before at the local estate and they had left a lot of venison at his house which he did not want, so this was put in the back of my car, which partly compensated for the very small fee that was attached to my midnight jaunt. Surgery can have some excitement as well as anxiety.

# In like a lion and out like a lamb

*In 1926 when the coal strike was at its height I had a sudden telephone call from one of my former professors. This was to see if I could go at once to England to take over an RSO job in St Helens, Lancashire. The matter was urgent because the Resident Surgical Officer in post must return home at once – his brother had died, and the practice and the dispensary attached to it must be filled without delay.*

*The professor knew that I was unemployed. I had just passed the first part of the FRCS and had been unsuccessful in getting any house job in England although I had applied for over 20 such posts – I was part of the postwar 1 bulge. It is good for the boys today to see that even in those days we also had our problems.*

*I agreed to go at once. I packed my bag with a few clothes and a lot of books, hoping to work for the final fellowship. I got the overnight boat to Liverpool, but what I did not know was that at midnight a general strike had been declared. At 7 am when I disembarked at the Liverpool docks there was no transport of any sort, so here I was, a small man with a big heavy bag, faced with a journey on foot of 20 miles. The position seemed hopeless until I discovered a small greengrocer's cart loaded to the top with bags of potatoes, carrots, sprouts, etc with a pony between the shafts and a rather unshaven gentleman in charge, but what did matter was that there was a small plate on one of the shafts which said " John Gribbon, Green Grocer, St Helens." I approached him and with great deference suggested that for £2 perhaps I might sit on one of the bags of potatoes as far as the hospital at St Helens. After a small monetary adjustment had taken place and when £3 had changed hands, I mounted the cart with my luggage and made my state entry into my job on a bag of spuds. I was told later that it was the first time that an RSO had arrived in such style.*

*As the miners' strike was the daily topic, and A J Cooke was the Scargill of that time, I decided that I should go to one of his meetings. It took place on the local Rugby League* football pitch. About 1000 people were there. I went in an old suit not to be conspicuous – this was not difficult as it was my only one. All went well and I mingled with the miners unnoticed until something happened that I had not foreseen. In those days miners did not stand, they hunkered down on their heels. They often did this in the mines working at the coal face and so as the crowd got ready for the speeches they all hunkered down, reducing the overall height to about half. I naturally did so with the others, but I did not realise that after 15 minutes of this I could not stand it any longer, and so the inevitable took place: I had to stand up and became the only visible figure in this vast audience – the very thing I had wanted to avoid. I had great difficulty escaping with nothing worse en route than being cursed both in English, which I did understand, and in Welsh, which I did not.

# Seeing the world at war

## A TEMPORARY SOLDIER

*Hat in the ring – sailing to the Gold Coast – away from the action – penicillin and surgery in the front line – India before independence*

# Called up

Having been a schoolboy during the first world war, I suppose the only valuable contribution I had made to the war effort was to pull flax, which was necessary to make the linen for aeroplane wings. (Sadly today flax seems to be no longer grown.) When I went to the university nearly half of my year were ex-servicemen, and hearing the chat of these men I and those of my age could not fail to develop inferiority complexes. I wished that I had done more, and most of my year must have felt the same as I did, because of those who graduated with me three became major-generals in the Royal Army Medical Corps, and another held a similar rank in the RAF medical branch.

With the threat of war in 1939 I threw my hat into the ring and offered to go, but without really thinking much about it. I never felt I looked much like a soldier, but I had an underlying feeling that I must do something. I heard nothing for some time but then suddenly one morning on my way to hospital for my outpatient session I was stopped by a friend, then professor of paediatrics, who was the local link with the War Office. This was to say that a surgeon was urgently required and my name had come up. I told him nothing could be more awkward – my wife in two weeks was going to have a baby, we had lost our first child, and I was anxious to be at home to help. His reply was an expected one: "Do you expect the war to stop to see you through your problem?"

There was no answer to that, but later on the same day a piece of luck arrived in that a man from my own year, who had gone to Persia with an oil company, suddenly decided that he would like to come home to join up. He had an FRCS and was eligible and so my paediatric friend rang up the War Office and asked whether he could at least temporarily replace Fraser, who obviously did not want to go. This was agreed. I followed his career to see what I had missed. He had two miserable years in Madagascar, but we later came together in Catania.

On first being called up I asked where they intended to send me and when I heard it was Finland I rapidly got a pair of "drawers woollen long" (DWL). After this initial delay and the arrival of a baby boy my real call-up came through, and I made no attempt to refuse on this occasion. By now I was intended for West Africa, where my DWL would have given me fatal hyperthermia and where the uniform was now shorts and a topee. The DWL were greatly appreciated some years later by War on Want. My tropical shirt had a vertical pad at the back so that the sun would not do any harm to the spinal cord. This spinal pad was detachable and, I assure you, was very soon removed. However, there was a delay before we set sail for the Gold Coast, because suddenly there was an enormous influx of troops into the north of Ireland. One reason for this was the rumour – unfounded – that Hitler might think of making a landing in the south of Ireland, and so I found myself, rather embarrassingly, a soldier in uniform on my own doorstep, unable to do my usual attendance at my two hospitals.

Before actually getting into uniform I had to be processed. I was seen by an elderly "dug out," a longstanding retired RAMC officer. When I say "dug out" I think perhaps this is an overstatement, as I do not think he had been fully "dug out" as yet. I happened to know him well, in fact we were very close friends. I visited him in his office and I could see that any physical examination was going to be an embarrassment to him. He quietly asked me if I had any varicose veins, and then somewhat sotto voce he asked me did I think I could possibly have a hernia – to go further than that was too personal. Yet he felt he must test my heart and lungs; a long hunt through a large drawer revealed everything but a stethoscope. He was obviously greatly relieved, but still felt he should do something. What about blood pressure? So, like

Ko-Ko in *The Mikado*, "with a frightful, frantic, fearful frown I bared my big right arm" and waited, but again luck was on his side – a sphygmomanometer could not be found. However, after a further feverish search through the rubbish in the drawer, he triumphantly produced a hank of coloured wool; I was able to tell him the colours, and so I was admitted as an officer to the RAMC. I was gazetted as a lieutenant but made a major overnight. My medical examination was not quite as bad as the story going round at that time that for the RAF now they did not examine the eyes, they merely counted them.

I spent two years in West Africa, where I went out first as a surgeon in charge of a surgical division to a large general hospital. Later it was decided that a consultant surgeon was required to coordinate the work in the four colonies – Gambia, Sierre Leone, the Gold Coast, and Nigeria – a job that required quite a lot of travelling. Although these four colonies were all in West Africa, and separated only by a piece of land, we were not allowed to fly overland as this was enemy territory. Some of it belonged to French West Africa, which was controlled by Pétain and the Vichy government, so we had to fly out to sea to bypass these areas. Britain at that time was trying to build up its forces in Egypt, and as all transport had to travel via the Cape – since the Mediterranean was not available – it was necessary that we should control the West Coast, depriving Hitler of potential submarine bases there.

Our trip out took almost eight weeks. The nursing sisters who followed two weeks later had the ordeal of being torpedoed just off Sierra Leone. All went well with them, however. The ship went down slowly, it was a calm tropical night, and beyond losing all their clothes and belongings they had an interesting experience in a calm sea in an open boat. Only one nursing sister was in uniform with her Queen Alexandra silver badge on her tunic. All the others were in evening dress, as the captain had told them that they were now in safe waters. This Queen Alexandra badge was important. There was much silver available in the Gold Coast and so we were able to get an impression of the badge by pressing it into a cuttlefish – the thing you give to parrots – and we then filled the mould with molten silver. This crude badge was a much prized memento later on. Our equipment was also sunk and had been salvaged, and our x ray machine and other pieces of apparatus gave permanent trouble because of the salt water. We had an emergency field kit sufficient for minor operations only.

One of our first patients was an African with a large penile sore, almost as large as an old five shilling piece. Knowing little about it, I thought it was possibly a tropical sore. No matter whether it was amenable or not to treatment, I felt that a quick circumcision would save time and so I asked one of the trainee surgeons if he would like to do the job. There were no gloves and I told him that if he held the parts in a swab he need never touch the skin. This he did until he started to sew up and in the process of doing this he pricked his thumb. In the evening in the mess before dinner he told me all about it. I asked him what he had done about it; it was just a slight prick, it did not even bleed, and he washed it well with spirit and iodine and then forgot about it. I looked at it myself that evening and nothing could be seen. Some three to four weeks later the officer in question went down with malaria, as so many did, and when I went in to see him he showed me his thumb – and now there was a small sore at the site of the needle prick. We took his Wassermann and it was positive, but 28 % of people with malaria do have a positive Wasserman reaction and so we waited until his malaria had been cured and then again took his blood. Now his Wasserman reaction was double plus; he had developed a primary chancre. As I said, we were two years in West Africa and so had ample time to give him at least three full courses of treatment. I was fully satisfied that he was in the clear. Nevertheless, when he returned home – being a very fine type of chap – he insisted on going to Netley for a full check-up, including even a lumbar puncture; fortunately with completely negative results. Many years later, when he was back home in general practice, he developed anginal pains and I am pleased to say that the War Office admitted that this was due to his syphilis contacted on war service.

We saw no enemy action whatsoever. Our surgery was the day-to-day problems that you get in healthy males between 18 and 45 years of age – hernias, piles, injuries, particularly sports injuries like knee cartilages etc. We saw no children's diseases, no geriatric diseases, and virtually nothing of the female sex. This was frustrating for several of us who had left a busy hospital appointment as well as a private practice. We all felt we had to "fill the unforgiving minute with sixty seconds' worth of distance run" – some were interested in gardening, flowers, fruit, etc; others in the birds and the animals of that area, or native customs. Some sort of sport was essential, especially for the "other ranks," whom we tried hard to keep away from the ladies of the town. We were fortunate in making close contact with civilian surgeons, and one or two of us did a day once a week at the civil hospital. Here we saw tropical surgery for the first time – guinea worms, tropical sores, deep muscle abscess, elephantiasis of the scrotum, yaws, vesicovaginal fistula. The last of these was seen in women who had had a female circumcision carried out as a ritual operation round about puberty. This had left them with a stenosed outlet to the vagina so that later when they came into labour the child's head was not able to escape and so from pressure a hole developed between the vagina and the bladder. Ureteric transplant into the colon was the order of the day. It was interesting to see almost no cancer of the breast; many of them were naked from the waist up. Appendicitis was hardly seen among the Africans when they ate their own food, but often a steward boy developed appendicitis when he joined our Mess with its European food. There was much trauma from accidents. The roads were bad, the vehicles were overloaded, and the Africans were not always competent drivers. Most of us, however, found the Africans very friendly chaps. We got on well with what they call today the Ghanaians. I still prefer to use the term the Gold Coast. There was much gold in the colony. Driving at night, one could see particles of it sparkling on the road in the headlights. The local goldsmiths were extremely adept and made a very good trade selling us bracelets, trinkets, etc. Sadly this was mostly of 22 carat gold and so soft that the bracelets often fell apart. In fact when I got home I had to sell one or two to be melted down as they were much too soft and too dangerous to be useful. Some of the members of the mess got their RAMC buttons made into pure gold. Some bought elegant coffee spoons in pure gold with the palm tree on top. Sadly the Africans took advantage of this, and the CO, who got his cap badge made in gold, found later that it was only gilt.

As far as games were concerned, the ground was too hard for rugby; soccer could be played, but hockey was the most suitable. The golf links were very dry and the greens were brown soil almost like cement. When I was playing golf one day my caddy cried out in great pain. He had stepped on a scorpion; it had raised its tail and stung him on the heel, a very common accident as these boys were all barefooted. There was no danger attached to this, but great pain. I took him quickly to the hospital and a deep injection of a local anaesthetic eased his pain almost at once. We all got wise to this problem, checking out our hats and shoes each day before putting them on.

We all were very malaria-conscious – long trousers after sundown and quinine daily. Sadly, when we were in the Gold Coast, Singapore fell and suddenly our quinine supply disappeared almost overnight. This was the very time that I got my first attack. I had been at a sports day at the local training college – Achimota – and I probably stayed too long. With the loss of quinine there was an interval before mepacrine became available. Although we knew the formula for this drug, we were prevented from producing it. Apparently international copyright or patent could even override the fact that we were at war with the country that produced it. I saw this same thing happen again in my hospital at home when Uroselectan for intravenous pyelogram was no longer available and again there was a hiatus before we stole the formula and produced it.

With the loss of rubber from Singapore another problem arose and that was the shortage of rubber gloves. I was asked, as I am sure were many others, to do one week's operating with bare hands; scrubbing the hands very carefully and filling the nails with soap. I disliked this very much. I am afraid I restricted my list to surface surgery such as hernias and the like. I felt that I could not in all honesty do a gall bladder or a stomach or any intraperitoneal surgery with bare hands even for research purposes. Incidentally, as it happened, the cases all did well so that I suppose we did learn something. It made me more than ever grateful to Halstead who had invented the rubber glove – not with any idea of asepsis but to protect the tender hands of Miss Caroline Hampton, his theatre assistant. The original gloves were produced by the Goodyear Tyre Company and were for this lady only. Later she married her boss. After that the male assistants also began to use the gloves; as one assistant said: "What was good for the goose was good for the gander."

In addition to helping in the civil hospitals we were able to help the Americans who suddenly came into the war, apparently rather unprepared as they had not yet organised any medical arrangements. A friendship developed which certainly to me was very useful later on. We also were able to help the Free French. As I said before, French West Africa became enemy territory, but French Equitorial Africa – in the interior and up to the Chad – was under the control of a black governor loyal to De Gaulle, so there was a constant coming and going to link up with that group. They were rather isolated and had quite inadequate communication with their own headquarters, so they were very glad of any surgical skill that we could provide. I still see regularly friends in Paris whose friendship dates from the contacts that we made then.

We missed much of the animal life as we were very much in the tsetse belt and never saw a horse or a cow. Sadly, though we were close to a magnificent beach which stretched for miles and was almost deserted, bathing was virtually forbidden. The nursing sisters were advised not to swim: they might themselves be drowned or they might endanger the lives of those who went in to save them. We in our own unit were particularly careful for a very sad reason. As I said, it took two months to reach our destination from Liverpool docks. On the boat there was a small canvas swimming pool which we all used from time to time, but one particular officer was in it almost all day. He was a massive chap, well built. He had got married only a few weeks before leaving the United Kingdom. On arrival we all went straight to the post office to send a telegram home. For simplicity these telegrams were numbered, and you chose the one most suitable – for instance, No 36 might be "All well, good journey, love." It was not too expensive: if delivered in two days it was £1, if delivered at once it cost £5. I am afraid most people settled for the £1 – you will see later why I mention this. On arrival at the hospital site the junior officers asked if they could go down to the beach. We had had no warning of any danger. I did not go down as the CO asked me to stay with him to organise quarters. Suddenly a message came for me to go down at once to the beach as three of our officers were there and were all unconscious. One was an eye specialist (now in Australia) and with artificial respiration he recovered. Another with the same treatment eventually began to breathe (he is now in Wales as an ENT specialist) but the third man, the one who had spent all his time in the pool and was a powerful swimmer, could not be resuscitated. Apparently with an enormous undercurrent he had been sucked out to sea, and he had decided that he could fight the waves and get back to shore; he thought he could do this as he was a very strong swimmer. What he should have done was to let the waves take him out further and then he could have been taken in later by an incoming wave.

As soon as we accepted that he was dead we immediately sent a telegram home to his wife to say that sadly her husband had been drowned. This of course was sent at first class rate, but the day after she had received this tragic telegram a further telegram arrived: "All well, good journey, love." This seemed to neutralise the first message. I was horrified when some eight weeks later I got a frenzied letter from a young bride to ask why her husband had not written after an apparently safe arrival. I had to write back a very sad and a very difficult letter.

We all slept in our camp beds that we had brought out with us. These became increasingly small and more uncomfortable after two years and we had to see that the mosquito net which was hung from the ceiling was carefully tucked into the bedclothes. A sheet or nothing was the usual cover.

The food was quite good. It had to be fresh, as meat, fish, etc could not be kept. The Gold Coast was hot and very humid. We could not grow certain vegetables; we never got potatoes, so we got our carbohydrates from the yam. There were marvellous fruits, however – paw paw, avocado, and bananas at a penny a bunch. The citrus fruits were delicious, and in a citrus farm I saw what can be done with grafting. On one tree there was one branch with lemons, another with oranges, another with limes, another with mandarins, and another with grapefruit. In fact our favourite drink in the Mess was Achimota, a fresh fruit drink made of all of these fruits squeezed together. You had to drink it at once as even overnight it began to ferment. It was interesting to see the loofah growing. I had never known what this instrument of torture which one uses in the bath came from, but it grew readily over the roof of our mess, like a convolvulus. It produced fruit rather like a cucumber, and when this was dried and the skin removed we had that piece of porous network which we now call the loofah.

At the end of my two years I was called in and told that I could now go home. I asked what I should do about that and was told that I should contact the transport officer and he would get me on a boat in six weeks or so. At this stage I remembered the Americans, who had told me that they would fly me home at any time when the time came for me to leave. I called on the officer in charge who immediately lifted the telephone receiver and in the usual American style asked when the next Kite was due to fly to the United Kingdom. I did not hear the reply but then I did hear him say, "Oh, you are full up; put on one 'overload' for this friend of mine," and he put the receiver down. Then he told me that I was to report at 3 am the next morning. I explained that I really did not wish to be an "overload" but he insisted that this was all right and was quite a normal procedure, because if the plane took off the ground you rapidly lost your body weight in petrol consumed. The word "if" was the only upsetting word, but I duly left the Gold Coast as an "overload" at 3 am.

# North Africa to East Anglia

On reaching London from the Gold Coast I visited the General. He told me I had done very well – he said that to everyone – and he suggested that after a short leave I should go out again. I had to tell him that under no consideration would I do that: I had been in West Africa for two years and I had never seen or heard a bullet fired in anger. The war was now in the desert where I might be of some service. He knew this himself very well, but he then had to tell me that he had no job for me in my rank, and if I insisted I must revert in rank. This I said I would do with pleasure, and I saw that he very much agreed and in fact I think he was somewhat relieved. I think he knew that West Africa no longer needed a consultant surgeon, as the original problem of protecting the Merchant Navy convoys no longer existed, and so I had my first leave, not knowing where I was going to go next.

On getting home I saw in the paper that a soldier on leave could apply for petrol for his car for a distance of perhaps 200–300 miles to allow him to contact his friends and relations. I went up at once to the office and met a young man who gave me the necessary form. I filled it in but when it got to the point of giving details of my car I had to say that my own car had been up on blocks now for two years but that my elderly father had kindly offered me the loan of his car, and he would visit his patients on a bicycle. The clerk, a little rat, quickly said what a clever idea it was getting petrol for the old man's car. He said I could not do that. I was furious, but realised that there was little I could do about it. Going down town afterwards I ran into a friend; I told him my story. He laughed and told me he never knew I was so stupid.

43

He said, "All you have to do is go to your father and ask him to make a present of his car to you."

I rushed out to my father, a document was quickly made out: "I, R M Fraser, hereby bequeath my motor car to my only son. SIGNED – ." I rushed back to the young man in the office. He said "What car are you now going to put it into?"

I said, "The same one as before," and he said, "Not on your life."

I quickly showed him my important document and I got the coupons for my petrol, and after two weeks I wrote out a similar document: "I hereby bequeath my car to my father. SIGNED – ." It was annoying at the time but amusing when you look back on it.

I had only been home about two or three weeks when I was suddenly called to the War Office for an urgent consultation. It seemed that a new drug, which I had not heard of, had been offered to the War Office for experimental use in the forward area on war casualties. This drug had now had about two years of experimental trial on selected groups of civilian diseases, including malignant endocarditis, osteomyelitis, venereal disease and so on, but now they wanted a larger and more varied field trial carried out and for the first time an adequate amount of the drug had become available. So Howard Florey decided, with the approval of the Medical Research Council, that a small team should take this drug overseas. As I was unemployed, and as they assumed that I had had a fair experience of the failure of the other drugs, sulphonamides and antiseptics, it was suggested that I might take charge of this research team.

I had been brought up on the rough and tumble of day-to-day surgery and doubted whether I could fill the requirements of pure science. I always felt that my co-worker Major Scott Thompson, a bacteriologist (later a professor in Wales) was the real scientist. The powers-that-be suggested that I should not try the drug on endocarditis (of which I did not expect to see a great deal) or osteomyelitis or VD. I thought that this last one was not a disease that was usually got by the troops when fighting on the beaches, so I naturally agreed. They also said they did not want it to be used on the enemy. To this I flatly refused to agree. As far as I was concerned the most deserving case, no matter what he was, would get the drug, and they had to agree to this.

Of course my work would not stand up to today's requirements. I did not take five very ill men and give them a placebo, another five men and give them penicillin. In fact, I gave everybody penicillin, but we could do that as we already knew only too well what the other drugs could do and could not do. When I took the drug to North Africa, Heneage Ogilvie had just started a regimen of treatment with sulphonamide and was not too pleased that penicillin was now going to replace it. Florey also appeared at this stage on the scene to oversee what I was doing. One evening in the Mess, Heneage, talking to me about Florey, said "This work always reminds me of that old Scottish hymn 'Can a mother's tender care cease towards the one she bear?'" I always found Heneage a very stimulating friend, a good debunker, although he could himself be misled – as indeed he was, over his work on the pylorus.

The team was virtually a two-man affair, the surgeon doing the surgery, taking swabs before and after, with a follow-up card to the surgeons who were to receive the casualty, and the other material going to Scott-Thompson, who all this time was doing the careful laboratory check-up. Of course we had no unit of our own, no beds, and so we were totally dependent on attaching ourselves to a working unit. It might be a small FSU (field surgical unit) in the forward area, or a field ambulance further back, or a CCS (casualty clearing station) on the lines of evacuation. We even started our work in a large 1000-bedded general base hospital in Algiers where we saw sepsis in its most advanced and entrenched state, deep sinuses unapproachable by surgery, with the patients dying of chronic sepsis. Our results were very disappointing and we soon realised that the further forward we could get the better would be the results. If the penicillin could go in with the bullet, all the better.

The relationships with the various units were most friendly, and although we were a nuisance the officers mostly enjoyed taking part in a completely new experiment. In one hospital the surgeon in charge suggested that he should allocate the cases for our research. I refused and suggested that we might move on to another hospital. However, the CO was most anxious that we should remain and so the problem was resolved. We had a very confidential and valuable document from the War Office which enabled us to contact directly the top brass so we could be informed in advance of where the next attack was going to be and we could thus place ourselves always in the right place. This meant hard work as we were busy all the time, whereas some of the FSUs, field ambulances, etc, did on occasions have a resting period.

It was annoying that our drug was in such short supply and it was rather frustrating later on to find that the Americans had much more than we had – and we were supposed to be the experimental research team. The Americans were able to use it on VD when this did not respond to other drugs. Our accommodation varied – at times we dealt with some of the casualties on the beaches, but if it seemed likely that we could not hold the beach head then we took them off on small boats to a hospital carrier. A hospital carrier is a small converted passenger packet boat, such as the overnight vessels that used to ply from Ireland to England. The bar or saloon was converted into a makeshift operating theatre with very unsuitable low ceilings, bad ventilation, and often a bad smell, but it was usually meant to be used only for overnight work. At Salerno, however, we had to work non-stop for two or three days, though this was quite unusual. The true hospital ship is, of course, a different affair entirely. It is really a floating fully equipped hospital capable of carrying the injured in comfort, almost luxury, to Australia and back.

At times we operated in tents, which I quite enjoyed. We could modify them to suit our needs, arranging entrances and exits and controlling the ventilation. Correct entrances and exits were very important, as in the dark the bearers must not collide with each other, nor indeed must they trip over hidden guy ropes. It seems a small point but it could be very important. Later, of course, as buildings such as schools became available we used them, as they had the great advantage of running water and other amenities.

The results of the penicillin cases are so well known that I must not enlarge upon them. The team went in with all the invasions. We started at Cape Pessaro at the point of Sicily, which we reached at 7 am, having sailed overnight from Malta. Having gained full control of Sicily, our next invasion was into Italy. We crossed the Straits of Messina to find no opposition. The boys enjoyed running up and down the streets of Reggio di Calabria, which had been almost abandoned. It was more like a bank holiday. As this seemed a long way from Rome, our main objective, it was decided that we should invade Italy further up on the west coast as this might save time, and so our next landing was at Salerno.

This was an entirely different affair; the enemy were prepared and expecting us, there was much primary resistance, and it was a long time before we felt we were in full control, since in the hills overlooking the town the Italians were still present in caves with their long-distance guns. These guns were on railway lines and could be brought to the mouth of the caves, and after shelling us in the town they retracted safely into the caves. Although the navy pounded these hills with very accurate shells, the final result was obtained only when the Ghurkas went up late at night in the dark with their kukris.

I personally at this stage took ill. I had no idea what it was, frightful pain in the back, etc. It turned out to be diphtheria. This had been a very common complaint in North Africa, with often the primary seat of infection a wound hidden under plaster of Paris on an injured limb, with paralysis of the soft palate sometimes the first sign. After a period of isolation in Salerno I was put in a small cowherd's hut, but was given superb care by the Queen Alexandra sisters.

After Salerno I was flown into Catania, where luckily I found myself under the care of my old friend Max Rosenheim, later Lord Rosenheim PRCP. Finally, when almost completely well I was evacuated to Cairo for two or three weeks' leave before flying home. I enjoyed Cairo very much; I felt completely well and I had nothing to do. Finally the great day came for me to ask for my passage home. I went to the transport officer, who seemed a very friendly chap, and he said he thought I could get a plane at 10 pm two days later. I paid up my bill at Shepheards Hotel and went out to the airport. When we were all assembled, my friend the transport chap got up and said he was sorry that he had been forced, at short notice, to take two Russian war correspondents and he could not refuse. He was very sorry, but two officers would have to be left behind; and so a senior RAF officer and myself, as we were going home on leave and of no importance to the war effort, were left behind. It was annoying having to go back to Cairo to get more piastres and not be sure that a room was still available in Shepheards. We were lucky to get a bed.

Two days later I saw the transport officer again and he said that he hoped in another two days I would be lucky. Again much the same thing happened; I thought it was going to as my nice transport chap was trying to avoid catching my eye. This time it was two American sergeants who were the experts, it appeared, in dealing with the Flying Fortress and were priority No 1; so back to Cairo again. The next time, before the transport officer could say anything I asked him what his excuse was going to be tonight. He was very embarrassed and then told me that he had been forced to take in a stoker and a very junior naval officer, a chap with a minimal, almost invisible, stripe on his cuff. I said to myself that this was the moment when I must "throw rank," and then the poor chap had to explain that these two young men – they looked like boys – had been in charge of a midget submarine which had done a marvellous job and they were both due at Buckingham Palace the next day at 11 am each to receive the VC. It was indeed with great pleasure and much humility that I went back to Cairo that night. It was an honour to give up my place to chaps of that sort. I finally did get back three days later and arrived home for a short leave, not very sure what was to be my next assignment.

I had not been actually told, but I knew the General had had a consultant post in view for me some time. This, however, was not yet ready. Probably they wanted to see that the invasion of Europe was a success before they started making full arrangements for the Burma campaign. I was therefore attached, again temporarily, to a general hospital which was preparing for Normandy. It was most important that the whole unit, and the surgical team especially, should get to know each other. This included the theatre staff who were such an important part of our work. They were all a new team to me. I was trying to assess the capabilities of my surgical colleagues and they were doing the same to me. The hospital was forming in Yorkshire but any other place would have done. While there I was called again suddenly to London and posted for a time to Cambridge to understudy Heneage Ogilvie who was now a major-general and was the consultant surgeon for Eastern Command, which comprised most of the east coast of England. I was given an interesting job there, which was to visit all the various hospitals on the east coast to advise them that they must make a plan to evacuate their hospital when "D" day came, so leaving adequate empty beds for the wounded evacuated from France. The government would supply them with the necessary blood afterwards. This was to ensure that after the invasion, if we had to evacuate our injured and were not able to retain them in France, we would have a series of empty

49

hospitals along the east coast ready to receive them, and for this purpose these hospitals themselves must make arrangements for hospitals further inland to take their cases. In every case the answer was, "Certainly, but when do we do this?"

That of course I did not know, and I suppose if I had known I could not have told them, as "D" day was then top secret. In fact, I myself at that stage did not even know that I was going to be involved in the invasion.

# He saw his own funeral

*I met him last year at a party. He is now a young-looking grandfather, but when I was billeted during the war in his mother's house in Cambridge he was a pilot in the RAF and had just been reported missing. At the party I heard the whole story.*

*He was one of a crew of seven in a Lancaster bomber which was on a night bombing raid on Germany, and it had been brought down over northern Italy. The plane was a complete wreck, but as it happened the crew escaped almost undamaged. It was only after the initial jubilation died down that the Germans realised that there were no bodies. The airmen had been hidden away at separate safe houses. This was easy, as at that time there was no real love between the northern Italians and the Germans. It required much quick thinking, as a house-to-house search would have discovered the airmen, with the usual retribution on the Italians who had hidden them. Rapidly seven graves were dug, and seven coffins ordered from the local undertaker. Two parish priests conducted the sad cortège of the coffins and a few mourners down the main street – I suppose it was really a case of "rentacrowd". The heavy coffins, filled with stones, were decorated with a few flowers; a final prayer was said at the graveside, and everyone was happy – no one more so than my friend Watty who, hidden behind heavy curtains, had witnessed his own funeral.*

# Forward in France

After my short sojourn in Cambridge I rejoined my unit in Yorkshire to await our instructions for Normandy. While still in Yorkshire we studied each day aerial photographs of the area around Bayeux where we were told our hospital site was going to be. We finally knew the area almost as well as if it had been a part of the English countryside. We located the water supply, the direction of evacuation to the harbour, and so on. Finally the great moment arrived and we entrained for the south, not really knowing where we were going. We arrived early in the morning in a wood, or a small forest, not far from Southampton. There was a canteen, good protective covering, and on the trees at regular intervals were loudspeakers. We were free to wander about but never to be out of earshot of the loudspeakers. We knew that when our name and number came up we must go at once to the assembly point and rush down to go on board our landing craft. Time was precious as these small craft, which could carry only a very few people, had to make many crossings each day.

The journey was exciting but uneventful. As the difference between the high and low tide on the French coast could be as much as 10 feet, it was not possible for our landing craft to be beached. We had to drop the ramp fairly far out and in moderately deep water. I, for one, found this quite unpleasant as in fact the water came nearly up to the nipple line. I complained about this to a very tall chap next to me, but I got no sympathy. All he could do was to point out to me how lucky I was to have so little of myself above the water compared with him who presented a much larger target for the enemy.

We were given a very good box of rations to keep us going until our own kitchen was working. One item I remember especially was a tin of self-heating soup. There was a spindle which projected into the soup and if this was touched with a match the soup could be brought to the boil in one or two minutes. This was much appreciated after our rather wet wade ashore.

Almost the first person I saw when I got ashore at Arramanches was Arthur Porritt. He was consulting surgeon to the 21st Army Group and had gone ashore very early. When he saw me he said, "What are you doing here? I thought you were off to India, but I am b – glad to have your help." The result was that I had two or three exciting months that I had not expected, in what I am sure was the best organised military medical exercise ever conceived. We had 22000 beds with never more than 14000 filled, so that my work with the hospitals on the east coast fortunately never arose.

A few days after my arrival a man came round the unit with masses of Camembert cheese in their little containers. Knowing – at least I thought so – that I was going back in a week or two, I bought about 10 of these cheeses to take home. I put them on the ground in my tent. I was rarely there in the daytime, and when I stumbled into my camp bed, beyond a strong aroma of Camembert I never saw them and in addition there was always a very thick ground mist, sometimes two feet deep. At the end of about three months I was hurriedly told to get back to London. I then remembered my Camembert. I hunted for them and found the little containers were all now completely empty. Worms had eaten their way through the soft containers and all my cheese was gone, so I had nothing to take back – except that before leaving I was able to buy a bottle of Calvados, the apple liqueur that is the speciality of Normandy.

I had a slight encounter shortly after arrival in Bayeux with a rather cross French baroness whose château adjoined our hospital complex. We had just completed the outside loos for the QA sisters and now had to find suitable camouflage – it is interesting what a surgeon has to turn his hand to. I never thought I would be a sanitary plumber; I suppose surgical plumbing in some ways is not so very different. The only thing we could do was to cut down trees and make the place more or less invisible. While we were doing this the lady in question came to me to complain. She said that we English in two days had done more harm and damage to her property than the Germans had in the past three years; and she was quite right. The Germans for their own good reasons had ingratiated themselves because this area was indeed most valuable for its milk, butter, eggs, and vegetables so necessary for the troops. They also paid them in large paper money, which only later they found was valueless. We paid them less but our money was at least true currency.

Reverting to the loos, we found a marvellous machine that I had never seen before. It was used for making deep circular holes in the ground, into which telegraph poles could be put. It was attached to the back of a lorry, it could be dropped down vertically, and was driven by the engine of the lorry, so that in a short time we had 20 circular holes some 10 to 15 feet deep. Now all that was required was a seat to put over them, and when we had arranged the surrounding camouflage we had indeed an elegant ladies' retiring room.

The hospitals were arranged along two roads which separated at a V junction. One road was naturally called Harley Street and the other Wimpole Street. Each hospital occupied many fields. There was a large entrance from the road for the ambulances and at the far end the exit opened again on to the same road. We built our tented hospitals along both sides of this road. We started with a large ambulance parking site. This led into the reception tent, where the triage took place, and from there the casualty was sent to the right place. If very ill, naturally he went to the re-suscitation ward which was close to the theatre. From the theatre the safe case could be sent to a nearby ward and the doubtful case would be returned to the intensive care unit. The simple cases when dealt with were discharged to a ward near the exit, never to be seen again. They probably would be

collected later and sent to England, especially if suffering from a simple fracture or something that could not go wrong. The first intake was 500 cases. This meant all hands to the pumps. A senior person had to be in charge of triage as the most important decisions about the man's treatment were taken there. Often for note-taking we pulled in the padres. The dentist we trained to be part of the anaesthetic team, and often the physicians, who had little to do at that stage, became most helpful for administration and other purposes.

Each surgeon was given some liberty in organising the tented theatre to suit his own ideas and his own team. My own particular theatre was H-shaped; the crossbar was the central supply area. A long table was covered with sterile towels and along one wall were about a dozen primus stoves, each with a fish kettle on the boil all the time. It was important not to have the primus stoves too close to the tent wall as at least one theatre was set afire and lost because of this. The senior QA sister was in charge. The heat was unbearable; I worked in shorts, naked from the waist up, with an apron, gloves, and mask, but for the nurses it must have been intolerable. On each side post of the H we had three operating tables. I found that a surgeon did best with three tables to himself. I was operating on one; on the next was the case that was finished, being dressed up, perhaps requiring a plaster of Paris. This could all be done carefully without hurry, and then the orderlies would carry the stretcher to the ward, which might be quite a distance away. If the surgeon had to wait he would have got frustrated, worrying people and being a general nuisance. It was much kinder to all if this could be done quietly and carefully without rushing. On table No 3 was the new case. While the surgeon was working he could be informed about the new case – where was the entrance? where was the exit wound? He could decide whether to have the man on his back or on his face, and the anaesthetist was also able to make the necessary premedication and other arrangements, getting the patient's teeth out, etc. (I remember one day, after a long session, seeing a large bowl filled with dentures which I am sure never got back to their owners again.) The intravenous anaesthetic was made up in a milk bowl in the morning so that all that was necessary was for the anaesthetist to fill his syringe.

Fatigue can be mental or physical. The first to faint was always the orderly. He, poor chap, had to stand about waiting for instructions. The theatre nurse was the next liability; again, she was waiting for orders and not fully distracted. The anaesthetist was next, but the surgeon never had mental fatigue sufficient to make him collapse, because his adrenalin kept working. At the end of a working session he was certainly fatigued, possibly more so than the others. There has never been any real agreement as to how long a surgeon can work with safety to himself and, more important, to the patient. One can do a single long stand if it is not going to be repeated, but if an invasion with acute casualties is going to last, for instance, 2 to 3 weeks, then an organised shift of duties must be arranged. I insisted on an eight-hour stint, then eight hours' sleep, and then eight hours' surgery. By this means we got 16 hours' work done in one day, and could do this indefinitely. Some of the young men thought I was getting old and could not do 12 hours, which they themselves wished to do, but I had had a good deal of experience both in North Africa and in Sicily and Italy and I knew that the standard of work and one's judgment deteriorated when one got tired, and we had no idea then how long the pressure was going to be kept up.

One patient I well remember was a German colonel. He had had an unfortunate encounter with a Canadian tank and had come out of it very seriously ill. After many pints of blood he recovered and we became close friends. The ward was a mixture of German wounded, English troops, and French civilians. Later one evening I did my round with hand-shaking and a friendly word from them all and a cheer as I left the ward. Next morning when I came to do my round it was very different. All the Germans turned their faces to the wall, even my German colonel. I could not understand it so I asked the sister and she could not explain it at all, but later she did remember that a young man had been admitted in the middle of the night. So we went down to see him. He was 18 or 19 year old with blond long hair, and very ill. Almost without examining him, I ordered three pints of blood to be given at once. I was about to put the needle into his arm when he wakened up to ask if this was British blood. When I said it was he said, "Take it away, I die for Hitler." Within one hour of his death my German friends were back to normal with friendly smiles again. I had never before realised the dread the average German soldier had of the SS. I heard a lot later from the German colonel. He was very hard up when he went home and I sent him some clothes for his family. Later he became wealthy and the process was reversed; in fact he later came to stay with us. The friendship persisted until he died a few years ago, sadly from a cancer of the throat.

Another case I remember because it was interesting was a young English captain who lay out very shocked with a gunshot wound behind his knee. Fortunately it was only when he got back into hospital that it started to bleed and then it gushed furiously from his popliteal artery. This is normally a difficult vessel to close but in this case we were able to do it and in addition we did a lumbar sympathectomy. He did well and was able to play squash again later. Each year I get a Christmas card from him; he is now 80 and he no longer plays squash but he is still very fit – one of the lucky ones.

I remember only the good and the bad. One I felt very guilty about was a fine soldier, a Belgian major. He had had a massive internal injury and his abdomen was filled with blood from a ruptured spleen. We got the spleen away, tied the pedicle and saw no other abnormality, but he died a few days later. Sadly I had missed a very small hole in the back wall of his stomach. It was hard to see but I felt there was no excuse. It was particularly sad as this man had fought as a Free Belgian all the war and now at last he was beginning to see the results of his work.

Another unusual case was a case of chronic tetanus in a young French civilian. I had never seen this before. He had sustained a glancing wound down the front of his thigh from an aerial missile and there was a considerably large open sore. His tetanus was mild. Suddenly, when talking to me, he would go into a minor spasm and then back to normal. He was in no danger and I thought I would try out penicillin in enormous doses, which I did for three days with no success, but after the wound was excised, leaving a nice clean surface, the spasms stopped at once and he made a complete recovery.

The surgery was a great advance on what we had done in the desert or in Europe, in that penicillin was now fully available and we had a daily supply of fresh blood from the United Kingdom. This we called the "milk round." Usually there were 12 bottles of blood in the container, but on one or two occasions there were 11 bottles of blood and one bottle of beer (this was not for the patient) – a nice thought.

58

We had not much time to see the devastation of the surrounding country but I do remember Caen completely flattened and the Gap of Falaise, which I remember best as I saw there so many dead horses. I was greatly upset by this, that these poor wonderful animals had to suffer for man's inhumanity to man. I revisited Caen some years ago and it was incredible to see it now transformed into a modern university city. The bombing and carnage that I saw there were the worst of anything that I saw in Europe or Africa. On a visit to Arramanches we were certainly impressed with the technology that had made the invasion possible, as, without a deep harbour for our heavy kit, Normandy would never have been a success as we would have had to invade it by the small landing craft which could only carry a small number of troops. It was interesting to see, when we walked ashore, a pipe line – PLUTO: "a pipe line under the ocean" – which carried oil for our tanks right from Britain to France; another wonderful piece of engineering.

Finally I got my recall to return at once. I had a sad farewell party and said goodbye to a wonderful unit. I heard not long afterwards, with the war progressing satisfactorily, that this unit moved up to Brussels. There they were put into a large elegant hospital, but I think most of the staff felt that it had lost its personality. They no longer felt that they were doing the forward exciting surgery which they had so much enjoyed in the Bayeux area.

I was told to make my own arrangements to get home, so I contacted the RAF. I went down to the airfield where there were masses of aeroplanes with no doors. I found a lot of airmen, but I had never seen so many depressed people. They had lost heart. These were the men who had been dropping troops into Arnhem, but with low cloud this was no longer possible. Finally I found an aeroplane that was going to the United Kingdom next day so I hitch-hiked a lift back to London.

# What would Hippocrates have done?

*He is now dead and so perhaps I can tell the story. He was professor of surgery and chief of staff in his hospital in Belgium at the time when it was overrun by the Germans. He was instructed by them to carry on with his daily work. If he himself was in touch with the underground it must have been only in a very minor way, although his wife, we must admit, was deeply involved, being one of the now famous "White Ladies."*

*One Sunday he was asked by a nice grey-haired old lady to come to her house for afternoon tea so that he could meet there a young man whom the old lady (she was the local link of the "escape chain") would be launching on his journey down the escape route to freedom in Switzerland. One should say that each person only knew the name of the person in the next town who would supply the escapee with a safe overnight lodging.*

*At the afternoon tea party the visitor spoke in almost impeccable English, but he did make one or two minor mistakes. One of these was when he said to the professor, "I will be in England in a week or two, and I could if you wish deliver a 'brief' for you to a friend." Although the professor himself spoke English with an appalling accent he had a very correct knowledge of English. The word 'brief' he knew was wrong. He realised that the man was a spy. If he was allowed to go down the escape route every person in this complicated chain would be shot or imprisoned and the whole escape line would be blown wide open. The spy must be liquidated.*

*The professor in his surgical team had only one assistant whom he could fully trust, and so he suggested to this registrar that he should take the visitor for a very interesting walk along a high path overlooking the Meuse and show him the sights. At one corner on this narrow path there was a sharp bend, and if the registrar could possibly slip at that point his companion could easily and "accidentally" fall into the river. The whole affair was carried out two days later according to plan. Sadly, instead of the Meuse being in flood*

it was frozen over, and so, instead of being carried away,
Mr X received a head injury only. He was brought into
hospital and was put under the care of our own professor.
After a few days it appeared that he was going to make a full
recovery, and so the professor suggested that a lumbar
puncture might be advisable. This was done, some CSF was
removed and replaced by some infected fluid. Next day the
patient was considerably worse; all the team now rallied
round with all the antibiotics available, but the patient finally
died. It was interesting that on several occasions during this
period inquiries came from the Germans regarding his

*progress, which proved that he was part of their team. Just before he died he admitted that he was a spy – he was in fact a citizen of a still uninvolved country.*

*Shortly afterwards the professor began to realise that he was now rather suspect and perhaps it might be wise if he silently slipped away. So it was soon after this that I made my first contact with him, when a foreign gentleman in a brand new RAMC uniform appeared for breakfast in the officers' mess at the Royal Herbert Hospital at Woolwich. His uniform was better than his English. From this contact a friendship of 40 years started, which ended only with his death.*

*If faced with a problem of this sort, I wonder what Hippocrates would have done.*

# Fly to India...

Back home again for two weeks' leave, I felt very differently this time. Somehow I felt a bit of resentment that I had to go out again and so far away. My wife and the two small children had had enough, I thought. My wife had done a marvellous job, having among other things to stand up to the bombing in Belfast, which was almost as severe as that of Coventry. We had let our home, and they had moved from one boarding house to another for nearly four years. As far as the children were concerned, I hardly knew them and the younger one did not know me at all. Unfortunately, this was a very common complaint with my contemporaries. So this leave, instead of being a happy one, was to me rather a sad one. I had also another problem and that was that my father was now well over 80. I felt I would not see him again. I was very close to my father; he was the man I admired most of all the people I knew, the man to whom, I can say with great pleasure, I owe everything that has come my way. I am afraid, when I went to say goodbye, I stopped the car on the way back as I could not prevent the tears from coming. Once away, however all that sentimental feeling had to go.

Before leaving for India we had a briefing at the War Office. The Director-General of the Army Medical Services was in the chair. When we had all sat down, he said that all the doors must be closed and he then sent someone to sit at each door. He then proceeded to tell us that a secret formula for a new drug had come our way. I rather understood, but I may be wrong, that this drug had been slipped out, or stolen, from a drug factory in Switzerland. He told us that this was a new drug called "222." It would free the British troops in Burma and India of all bowel and malarial problems. He said that while the British soldier could shoot standing up the Jap would still be squatting with his diarrhoea. He told us that, in the hospitals in Burma at that time, for every one British soldier in hospital with a bullet or surgical injury, there were 130 others in hospital with general medical problems such as skin diseases, bowel problems, blood diseases, and malaria, and that "222" would deal with them, but that on no account must this formula get into enemy hands; and with a few other remarks our briefing ended.

A few days later I was told to report to Poole Harbour and stay overnight and be ready to leave for India at 6 am the following day. This time I went out with only a suitcase – no camp bed or mosquito net was necessary. At Poole Harbour we got into a Sunderland flying boat, now sadly almost an extinct species, I am told. The cabin, which occupied most of the flying boat, was centrally placed; it was oval, and almost the size of a small room. We all sat round it on rather uncomfortable aluminium seats – bedpan seats as they were soon named. There were 20 of us for the 40 seats. On each empty seat between the passengers there was a small wooden keg with "222" clearly written on the side. We all felt that this barrel was of as much value to the war effort as were any of us, and I as a surgeon knew that it was going to do much more good than I was likely to. In the empty space in the middle of the Sunderland was a space for our luggage, and a packed lunch.

It was an exciting way to travel. The flying boat first makes a short journey to produce waves, a mildly rough sea, as it cannot take off from a flat surface; a quick trip with the throttle fully open, and the flying boat takes off into the air. We flew the whole way just above sea level. We skirted France and Spain, entered the Straits of Gibraltar and touched down in the harbour there just in time for lunch. We had an afternoon tea there and then in the hills above Gibraltar we had an evening meal, entertained by the monkeys. It to me was almost as good as a Hellenic trip. The pilot was an interesting chap called Brown, a brother of the famous Brown of Alcock and Brown.

Gibraltar was still with its semi-peacetime atmosphere, except that throughout the night we were wakened regularly, or rather irregularly, by the various ships in the harbour which would suddenly start their engines, putting the propellers into action. At that time in the blackout there was a danger that someone might slip out and attach a sticky mine to the propeller area and so totally immobilise the ship. It prevented us from sleeping but it was obviously well worth while. We got up again at 6 am for our second day, a repeat of the day before, and this night we spent on a small island called Djerba, just offshore to Tunisia. There was nothing on the island but lobsters and sponges. We had some of the former and I bought the largest sponge that I had ever seen. (I thought that it would be a great success. It was a total failure. When I brought it home and my wife filled it with water it was so heavy that it broke into two on the first occasion.) We had a midnight bathe in the Mediterranean and then to bed. I am told that today this island is a tourist resort with pleasure beaches and large skyscrapers.

Next day, again up at 6 am. On the evening of the third day we arrived on the Nile near Cairo, and then on the fourth day off at 6 am, taking the air after roughing up the smooth surface of the Nile. On the way, our pilot Mr Brown made a small diversion to show us the actual Garden of Eden. It was at the junction of the Euphrates and the Tigris as far as I can remember. The Garden of Eden was to me a very brown and barren area. I could not see a tree that might bear a fruit that would have tempted Adam, much less myself; nor indeed, could I see a fig tree that could have given Eve any protective covering. In the afternoon we arrived at Bahrein where we spent the night in an army camp – not Hellenic standard but we had the pleasure of a wonderful bathe in a hot lake some distance out of the town. On the fifth day, and our last, we left as usual at 6 am, arriving at Karachi, and from there on by air overland to Delhi, where I reported to the General.

What happened to my "222" I do not know but I should

say, as you have probably guessed, that "222" was indeed DDT, and within one year the ratio of medical to surgical cases in the wards had fallen to 30:1 as compared with the original 130:1, and when I left after one year the ratio had come down to 10:1, but even that was rather sad – it still meant that 90% of the patients admitted were suffering from a medical problem and therefore possibly a preventable disease.

India is V-shaped. It was divided into two across the middle; the lower half was Southern Command. In the old days the famous North-West Frontier leading up to Afghanistan was the great problem. This, however, was now quiet and it was the northeast corner which was the dangerous area, with the Japanese now the enemy. In between these two there was a vast territory called Central Command with its general headquarters based at Agra, and this I found from the General was to be my area for the next 12 months. There had been a consulting physician there for a long time before I arrived, for the reasons that I have given, and this was sensible, but now with more enemy action impending they felt that a consulting surgeon was necessary. The consulting physician was Bernard Schlesinger, a paediatrician from Great Ormond Street. We became very close friends, which only ceased with his death a few years ago. We each stayed in a different hotel in Agra in considerable comfort. I cycled to my office in the cantonments daily; Bernard went by motor car – a wealthy chap. When he left India he gave his bearer his motor car as a present. I was only able to leave my bearer a second-hand bicycle. It was wonderful after dinner to be able to cycle only two miles to gaze at the Taj Mahal with the moon coming up behind it and hear the frogs croaking. I did this often, as living by myself I felt very lonely in the evening.

We had a vast area to cover. This was done either by staff car or by train or by small aeroplane. The consulting physician and I very seldom went together; we felt that it was easier for the commanding officer of the hospital that we were visiting to deal with one of us at a time, and we were able later to compare notes together. Again our patients were

66

not acute injuries – a great contrast to any of my previous jobs in Italy and France. I suppose it was a good preparation for getting back to civil life again. The Indian Army in Central Command was lucky in that the officers were able to have their wives and families with them, so I was involved sometimes in the treatment of wives and children: the occasional gall bladder, a thyroid or two, a few cancers of the breast, one or two caesarean sections – a real contrast to the surgery of the beaches. We were busy not so much because of work but on account of the long distances we had to travel. Our own area went as far as Benares in the east to the Indian state of Bikanir in the west. I found Benares very interesting. It was so different from anything that I had seen before. One got used to seeing a dead body being carried down the street to be carried to the ghats on the bank of the Ganges, later to be burned on a funeral pyre. If they could afford good wood and plenty of it the body could be burned completely, but if the wood was green and scarce the body was sometimes only charred before they threw it into the Ganges.

In Bikanir the maharaja was a man of middle age, the son of the great maharaja whose picture appears in many of the photographs of the first world war when the various peace treaties were being signed. This maharaja had not joined in the war himself but he very kindly at his own expense provided us with one or two hospitals, not only for British and Indian troops but also one for Japanese prisoners. The Japanese wounded were very ill men, as most of them tried to commit suicide rather than be taken prisoners. If I was the most important visitor to Bikanir on a visit there I was asked to be the guest of the maharaja and stay at the palace, but if there was someone more senior then I was put up in an elegant guest house hotel. Visits such as this were indeed the highlight and a pleasant contrast, as on tour we usually slept in a tent attached to the general hospital and had our meals with the staff, but I should say at once that these visits were few and far between.

I did a certain amount of lecturing in India, and one of my talks naturally was on penicillin, not yet available there. For this purpose I had brought with me my lantern slides and a small bottle of penicillin with a shiny silver top. One morning I found that this small bottle was missing. I had put it on the dressing table, which was close to the window, before going to bed at night. I complained next day to the bearer when he brought me my morning tea. He was able to explain it all easily. A shiny object always attracts a monkey, and through my open window a monkey had stolen my precious penicillin. It was the last of the original impure penicillin that I had taken to North Africa. I had kept it as a souvenir just to show how impure the original stuff was. The original powder looked rather like mustard and when diluted with water and injected it gave agonising pain, just the same pain as mustard would have given. So my precious bottle was gone, never to be seen again.

We were lucky having Kashmir and the hill stations for possible holidays. I did one short trip there up to Srinagar and then to Gulmarg by pony trek. Staying on a house boat was interesting, but as a doctor I found it hard to get the insanitary possibilities out of my mind. I did some shopping there. I was advised that fur coats were cheap so I went to "Suffering Moses," one of the leading emporiums there. I selected a coat and then told him that I had been told that he parcelled his goods up only in gunny or sacking before sending them to the United Kingdom and they would often lie on the docks at Bombay and were often partially eaten by the rats before they reached England. He told me to come next day and I would see that it was sufficiently done up in a nice tin box. This I did, and left well satisfied. When it arrived about three months later it was covered with some sacking – no tin box. He had used this one and only tin box before and since to hoodwink many others like myself. The fur coat was not a success – you cannot win all the time – and it was quietly given away some time later. However, I was lucky with some of my presents – delightful handmade rugs, some pashmina for dresses, table mats, and so on. There was at that time an English lady in Kashmir who directed the local workers. She had the ideas and they had the skill, and all they needed was supervision.

I can see why many people love India. The climate was good, there was freedom and originality, and with courteous servants life seemed easy – too easy for many. I remember in Simla seeing a not very strong-looking Indian with a thing like a halter over his shoulders with two large hooks attached to it, and he was climbing a hill with a piano on his back, with the two hooks holding it in place and with his back taking its full weight. It is a sight I have never forgotten. The food I got to enjoy, although I thought that possibly the West African curry was better, and I think most of us preferred the West African mangoes; the Indian mangoes at times had a somewhat turpentine taste about them. One thing I did not appreciate was mulligatawny soup for breakfast. This was a relic from the old days when an officer with a hangover from the night before in the Mess could be rapidly cured, they said, by mulligatawny soup. I quite agree that it certainly would frighten away anything at that time of the day. While I was there the country was just working up to independence, and it was terrifying to see the speed with which this was taking place. There was one journey that I did frequently. I got into a certain station at midnight for my train to Agra. My bearer used to go along the train and find a sleeping compartment; often there were four junior Indian officers in the four bunks. He would go in and say that the brigadier sahib would like a bed. All four would jump up, each one of them offering his bed. Only six months later, and now with slogans on the walls "England go home," "Britain get out," I would go to the same station for the same train. My bearer would make the same request but the four young officers somehow could not be wakened, and so the brigadier sahib slept on the floor. This change all took place over a period of about four months. Sadly those slogans on the wall I see now in my own town – what a tragic world we live in.

I met Lord Mountbatten only once during my tour in India. It was in the state of Bikanir. He had come through with Lady Edwina, and as she was going to visit the local hospitals the next day in her capacity as chief lady in the Order of St John, I was asked to be in attendance. We had a delightful dinner in the open air, on a raised grass mound, for some 20 people the night before. One of the courses was chicken in aspic – the most dangerous food that one can eat in any hot country; in fact, in any laboratory it would be much better for growing organisms than what is put into those small Petri dishes. Lady Edwina and her entourage and myself were to meet at 6 30 am next day. I arrived, waited some time, and finally the lady in question arrived, but alone. Her entire party, and I am sure many others, were all down with the D & V – diarrhoea and vomiting. I thought what a really strong person she was, tough as old boots. I hope she thought the same of me. She was perfect in her approach to the troops. She would whisper to me did I think he was a Pathan or perhaps a Madrasi, or perhaps a Ghurka, etc, and for each she had just one or two words in their own language. I admired her greatly.

This ability to talk to the Indian soldier was also what

appealed to me most about General Auchinleck. No matter what province the men were from he was able to speak to them in their own language. He was a splendid front line general, and the men would have followed him anywhere. To me the "Auk" was a man enormous in every respect. (Some years ago, when I was on a short holiday in Marrakesh, I heard that he was living there and I paid him a visit. He was living in great discomfort, a sad contrast to the man I had known in India. He was now very deaf. He did not know me, naturally, but welcomed me as I brought greetings to him from his cousin in Ulster. With his extreme deafness it was hard to make much contact with him. He died some three months later.)

When in India I saw two cases that I had never seen before, cases of true hyperthermia. They occurred in two marines who had got on to the train at Bombay to go north. Firstly, the fan in the carriage was not working; but secondly, and more important, they were drunk and not able to realise their problem. When there was no way of keeping cool, the usual method was to have a zinc container – a sort of foot bath – on the floor of the carriage into which one could stick one's feet, and the ice in it could be replaced at most railway stations. When finally these men reached Agra and came under my care, they were completely decerebrate; body temperature I suppose had risen to anything from 105 to 110 °F. Presumably this coagulated their protein just as hot water does to an egg. I never heard the final result but they were returned to the United Kingdom at once to some mental hospital for life, or for as long as they had to live.

Talking of alcohol, a man from my own medical school got into trouble once in this respect. He was coming home late at night from a very good party. He went into what he thought was his bungalow (they all looked alike), he sat down and then saw a whisky decanter, so he helped himself generously. At this moment the area commander, a brigadier, came in and saw that the last of his whisky, which was in short supply, one bottle per month, had now disappeared. Very little was said – there was nothing to say – but my friend was on a plane home next day to the United Kingdom.

Finally came my own great day to get home. Was it going

to be another Hellenic trip? Not so. A plane from Delhi through to London with one stop for refuelling at Bahrein. It is sad that modern technology has spoilt much of the pleasure of travel.

My next step naturally was to be demobilised and get back to civil life again, and get to know and be known by my family. I was told to report to the barracks where I would be provided with a grey pinstripe suit, socks, shoes, a shirt and tie to match. I was now supposed to be ready for civil life and to look like a gentleman.

# Swings

## CHANGES IN MEDICINE, SURGERY, AND FORTUNE

*Disappearing diseases – and fleas – smash-and-grab raids –
Corrigan's button – how to pass with the scones or an
international cap*

# Diseases that have disappeared

When I was away for the war years from the Children's Hospital my deputy kept the waiting list down but left behind some 17 cases of hypospadias. This was an operation that before the war I never did to my satisfaction, and certainly not after it, not having operated on a baby of any sort during the war, much less still a child with a complicated penile deformity. I felt that I must get expert help. Denis Browne very kindly agreed to come over and have a "field day" – three "field days" – doing my hypospadiac cases. They were a memorable three days. Operations were done morning and afternoon, there was a lunch at the hospital attended by all the registrars in the province, and a pleasant social dinner in the evening. It was an occasion still remembered with gratitude by us all. Denis refused to take a fee but did go home, I am glad to say, laden with a ham, a turkey, and a good selection of lobsters – possibly more interesting.

Working at the Children's Hospital had been my first surgical appointment. This was the rule in Belfast. It also happened in other parts of Britain, particularly Edinburgh. It was a bad system, as it meant that the young man as yet not fully trained was put in charge of one of the most difficult parts of surgery. Infantile surgery at that time included intussusception, congenital pyloric stenosis, Hirschsprung's disease, hare lip and cleft palate, and club foot, to mention only a few. This fell to the lot of a young man with often also a young anaesthetist. Fortunately, this has all changed and today paediatric surgery is not a branch of general surgery but a real entity on its own.

In the pre-National Health days there was no money to be

75

made from children's surgery. The parents were young people who had not yet made their way in the world. (Very different was the surgery of the aged, for instance prostatic surgery, where the old man now with some money was willing to pay well for his operation.) One of my seniors when he left to take up his appointment in the main teaching hospital told me that he had made nothing when on the staff of the Children's Hospital except for an occasional circumcision. For this he said he used to charge five guineas – five shillings for doing the job and five pounds for knowing how to do it. (That same man, when a young registrar, did a very valuable piece of work when just before the first world war he was working in the anatomy department and produced "Man 50." This was an anonymous cadaver, which he put into a wooden box slightly larger than a coffin. The box was then filled with water, and after some time in the deep freeze, when fully solid, the whole box and contents were cut into one inch cross-sections starting from the head and going down to the knees. These famous cross-sections were produced at every examination. They gave us then a similar cross-section of the body to that which we get today from computed tomography. He was a man before his time.)

My two days a week at the Children's Hospital were well known by the family as these were the days when I brought home the fleas. It was impossible to avoid this. The average woman who attended came in a large black shawl, from the depths of which she produced a miserable infant. Although one tried to keep at a distance beyond "one flea hop," it did not work as the woman with a flap of her shawl gave the flea a flying start compared with the standing start of its competitors.

On such occasions, I always thought of Laennec who invented the stethoscope. To start it was a wooden monaural tube 12 inches long. Laennec thought that Hippocrates, who put his ear directly on the chest, was "indelicate and even disgusting." Today with longer and longer rubber tubes to our hearing aid we are now apparently at a safe distance. But one must be honest: the unfortunate flea seems to be on the way out, now almost an endangered species.

Out of the depths of the black shawl often would appear a child with glands in the neck in one of its many stages – lumps, discharging sinuses, and so on. Often a child with a paralysed leg or arm. I never did an outpatient session without seeing one or two cases of glands in the neck, and certainly every two weeks I would see a new case of poliomyelitis. It is hard to realise today that, with a drop of fluid on a lump of sugar, this condition has totally disappeared.

My attachment to the Children's Hospital was one of my most enjoyable appointments. I built up a large collection of children with interesting conditions whom I kept coming to the hospital, more for my good and for teaching purposes than for anything I was able to do for them. They were mostly children with bony abnormalities – dwarfs, achrondoplasiacs and others – and I kept them coming long after they had exceeded the age limit; in fact they became friends.

The acute surgery of children seems to have changed somewhat. There do not now seem to be so many cases of intussusception. I noticed in an article recently that in Nottingham with its large population there were not more than one dozen cases in a year. At operation we found that there were many glands in addition to the intussusception and I think it was the glands that helped to produce the telescoping. Possibly now glands, like tuberculosis, have disappeared.

Diseases seem to disappear in different ways. With the great publicity attached to insulin and liver, diabetes and pernicious anaemia were under control almost overnight. Sadly the diabetic problem is not yet solved. Penicillin had an interesting but very different background. There was an incubation period of 14 years and even when it was accepted there was a further period before adequate production was available. This British invention, the result of the cooperation of a Scot, an Australian, and a Russo-German emigré – a triad in which cooperation was not always the right word to use – is certainly the discovery of the century. Acute sepsis before that date was incurable. I remember when I was in my first year at the university – I was still in bed – my father called in to see me. He told me that three hours earlier I had lost a great friend. The man who had brought me into the world, and a close friend of the family, had pricked a finger at an operation three days earlier and was now dead. It was an occupational hazard at that time, particularly with pathologists. With red lines running up the arm we were really powerless. Some people, including myself, made multiple slashes in the arm through skin and fat and down to the muscle, working on the theory that if we could stop the lymphatics then we might prevent the infection getting into the body. One man went even further and suggested that the final entry of the lymphatics was by the lymphatic duct into the venous system in the neck, and so Da Costain suggested his famous operation of draining the thoracic duct externally, which he called lymphaticostomy, a brilliant idea but quickly abandoned when it was found that the lymphatic fluid was sterile – a devastating disappointment.

Hand infections in my day were common. We taught our students all about the palmar spaces and the technique of how to get at the hidden pus. This is no longer a real problem. A carbuncle today is never seen, yet I used to teach students how to deal with it either by a cruciform incision lifting up the edges of the flaps or perhaps the complete circular excision. Erysipelas, a dangerous disease, no longer appears in the text books. As a student, when I heard my teachers talk of hospital gangrene, I thought they were talking of the Crimea. Students today, if I talk of a carbuncle, will think much the same.

The complications of acute infection have also disappeared. With pneumonia no longer a problem, empyema has become almost extinct. No longer do we discuss the variations in rib resection or intercostal drainage, and all the minute detail that we went into at that time. The same applies to the mastoid operation. How many great reputations were made by these operations. Sir William Macewen of Glasgow was a great man who gave his name to the mastoid incision and to his operation of osteotomy for bow legs, so prevalent at that time in Glasgow, not to mention his series of cures of brain abscesses which has never been improved upon. With bow legs no longer a problem, the Highlander can now wear his kilt with greater pride.

The hunchback of tuberculous origin is no longer seen. Why it had a sinister significance in literature I do not know. It was at one time common, since the patient with the tuberculous spine survived if his spine collapsed and produced a hunchback because it cured the disease; in fact, those who did not produce this deformity mostly perished.

When I was a student we kept tuberculosis at the back of our minds all the time. Norman Walker in his book on dermatology said, "If you see a rash keep syphilis in your mind but do not have it on the brain." I think we had to do the same with tuberculosis: a pain in the abdomen, in the head, in a joint, in the chest – tuberculosis had to be excluded. I perhaps was more sensitive to this problem than others. My mother had died of tuberculosis, and my wife and I had the extreme sorrow and agony when our first, and then only, child died of tuberculous meningitis. The paediatricians had kept reassuring us that all was well, that it was a case of pink disease, but with the onset of neck rigidity the diagnosis became all too obvious. This is a loss that is as poignant to me today as it was 60 years ago.

Although the organism causing tuberculosis was discovered in 1882, it was 60 years before a cure was found; so when we talk of a cure we must not assume that if we find the cause we would automatically know the cure. A chronic disease like tuberculosis leaves its scars for 40 or more years of the life of a patient; the stiff knee, the hunchback, the scarred neck, the missing nose from lupus, the deformed chest from thorocoplasty, all are still to be seen, but once that generation goes then this should all be a thing of the past.

In my day chronic sepsis was a sad problem. In the hospital was a ward called "Septics" with 20 beds or so. It was discreetly hidden away from the mainstream. It was a ward not visited regularly by the chiefs but daily by the house surgeon or registrar. The patients were all of long standing with inaccessible sinuses which were discharging into the depths of the chest, the abdomen or down to some deep-seated bone disease, often with long tortuous tracks. They drained day and night into dressings or at times into a container. As no antiseptic or antibiotic was available and surgery was thought not to be possible, these patients, some of them young people, went into that ward to die, and sadly there was always a waiting list in the hospital proper for a bed in that ward. They mostly were dying from amyloid disease of the liver.

80

Chronic sepsis still exists today but surgery is bolder and we can now also produce the antibiotic cover, but one must emphasise that antibiotics will not deal with bad surgery – a thing that is at times forgotten. Laudable pus was really true. If the body did produce pus then there was some resistance. Sadly, doctors did not always do their best to help the "Vis medicatrix Naturae"; they at times were doing the reverse. I am afraid I myself have put pure carbolic on wounds, certainly doing more harm than good. I do not suppose that the hot boracic fomentation, the linseed poultice, or the drug firm's Antiphlogistin did any good. Nor indeed did the formation of a fixation abscess in an area with the hope that this might make a focal point and so an area of discharge. The perinephric abscess was a not uncommon lesion. The organism floating in the system found an area of poor resistance, the fat around the kidney. An opening and good drainage were all that was necessary, but often it required a search before the fons et origo mali was found; often the trouble had arisen from a small infected boil or other mild infection which at the time of the major operation had almost disappeared.

Venereal disease was badly treated in my day because we had no easy cure. The non-treated patients in many cases developed a urethral stricture. I am ashamed to say that the rough instrumentation and strong antiseptics in use at that time often meant that more harm was done with treatment than by the disease itself. The douche, if used too energetically, would occasionally carry the infection to an area it would not have reached of its own accord. A vast collection of aging gentlemen with their strictures was usually seen on a Sunday morning – "The Bible Class" – when they came to hospital to have their strictures dilated. It was a junior's job and often he was regaled with stories from these gentlemen telling him how they had taught his seniors to do the job. For some it was an enjoyable, almost social, occasion where they met their friends, and some kept coming long after it was really necessary.

# Owlie

Many years ago I was called to the country late at night to see a maiden lady of 50-odd years of age with a suspected acute appendicitis. The patient lived with her elderly mother in a large mansion locally called "The Castle." This was approached by a long avenue, which on the other side opened out into a stony promontory on the open sea.

On arrival my first reaction was to the unpleasant smell in this stately home. The second was to the eerie sound in the darkness of mice scuttling all over the place. Going up the elegant staircase I did not touch the balustrade because of bird droppings.

When I had finally finished examining the patient in her bedroom I realised for the first time that we were not alone, but were watched from the top of a large wardrobe by a pair of dark eyes belonging to a very unfriendly owl, which was taking in all that was happening. It was then that the patient explained that Owlie was indeed part of the establishment, having been saved from drowning when, with a broken wing, it had been almost carried out to sea. To feed the owl, mice had been brought in and kept in a cage, but they soon escaped and in farmyard language became "free range." The elderly mother and daughter were quite unable to cope with the problem.

The patient did have an acute appendix and was taken away in the back of my car for immediate operation. In her absence the old mother, unable to live alone, invited a nearby neighbour to live with her until her daughter came home. This visitor was a London-trained retired physiotherapist and a close friend. On taking her seat at the breakfast table next morning she occupied the daughter's place, and was immediately dive-bombed by the owl – and for the 10 days she was there had to wear for her protection an old army tin hat, a wartime relic that was in the house. On the patient's return, still convalescing, the owl was overcome with joy. It brought its finest token of appreciation and deposited a dead mouse on the patient's bare bosom.

The patient, her mother, and the owl are now dead; but the physiotherapist is alive and well, and still likes to tell at her tea parties of the time when she had to wear a soldier's tin hat for breakfast.

# The changing face of surgery

Surgery has changed so much over the years that it is hard at times to keep abreast with it all; but this is the charm of surgery, that it has a growing edge. It gives it an excitement and an attraction for anyone with intelligence. Anatomy, sadly, has not changed; the body seems to be just the same as in those mummies we see displayed in Cairo or other places; the chair of anatomy no longer has the same appeal for doctors. I say this sadly as it was my favourite subject, but today in some places we see that the professor is a dentist, a vet, or a scientist. I personally feel that the correct person for the chair of anatomy is a surgeon who has retired at about 60 years of age. His assistants, young men, can deal with the nitty-gritty of the minutiae, but the surgeon will make the major organs live again and show that they have a real raison d'être. The duodenum is not a hollow piece of tubing measuring some twelve thumb breadths, it is a tube which often develops a hole in it as the wrong time and if that hole is not repaired the patient will die.

The advances in surgery arise for the most part from ancillaries. The surgeon himself still has only got the same five digits on each hand; the patient still has, more or less, the same disease processes. The ancillaries include anaesthesia with its endotracheal tubes, its hypothermia, its relaxants. There is better lighting, better ventilation, a series of endoscopic instruments, with fibreoptic visual aids. There is more efficient suction and diathermy. There is a vast umbrella of antibiotic cover. The intensive care unit is ready day and night for preoperative and postoperative care. These and many others have changed the face of surgery. With extracorporeal bypass circulation, as long as the brain and kidneys are allowed to function it seems that the rest of the body can be thrown out of action to allow any major repair to be carried out.

Preoperative techniques have changed. In my day there was much fuss and discussion over the best solution for skin preparation. Some chose iodine, others picric acid or gentian violet. Iodine was in short supply when I was a student and so my unit was using picric acid with a high percentage of skin rashes. The gynaecologists were using Bonney's blue paint, which they thought had special properties. It became very popular with all except the nursing staff who could not get the stain off the towels, which were permanently ruined. Victor Bonney was one of the leaders in gynaecology at that time. When I first met him he called me "darling," which to me was unusual as I was not that sort of chap, but I later found he did that to all, both males and females, which is, I suppose, part of the accoucheur's bedside manner. With Bonney's blue paint so much in vogue, a London gynae-cologist was on top of a London bus when he overheard a lady beside him saying to her friend, "I got my back passage painted blue last week, and next week – " At this stage he put down his *Times* to hear better. It was disappointing, as she went on to say, "next week they are going to do the pantry and scullery in the same colour." He resumed reading the Court and Society column. This story is of course apocryphal, as no London gynaecologist has ever been seen on a London bus.

Another gynaecologist whom I saw on several occasions was Blair Bell. I was resident surgical officer in a hospital near Liverpool at the time and he was called out occasionally to do a private case. We had a very good strong table in the theatre, firm and solid, which in fact I was using daily, but he always got his driver to bring in from the boot of his car an antique Heath Robinson affair which had to be articulated rather like a Meccano set and when erected was totally unsafe. It would certainly today not pass its MOT. On one occasion he took a great fancy to the theatre sister and asked her to become matron of his private nursing home in Liverpool – an honour which she could not refuse. I called to see her for a cup of tea some weeks later. I found her in tears. He was treating all his cancer patients at that time with lead; they were all developing lead paralysis, dropped wrist, dropped foot, blindness. She found this very depressing and very hard to take. This was then an up-to-date treatment for gynae-cological cancer. It arose from the fact that lead was a popular back-street method of producing an abortion and so it was suggested that if it killed fetal cells it might therefore kill the embryonic cells of malignant disease. I do not think it had had any extensive experimental trials and it fortunately did not last long. It was a good idea in theory but useless in practice.

To open a joint in those days – for example, a cartilage operation – the skin had to have a three-day preparation. Naturally, with no antibiotic cover a septic joint became often an amputation, so extra care quite rightly was necessary. Anaesthesia was primitive; sleep was induced with chloroform and followed by open ether or sometimes with a chloroform and ether mixture. On the side table was a bottle of castor oil as the eye was often touched during the operation to see the pupil reaction, and usually next day there was a severe conjunctivitis from this and from the ether vapour if the lids were not kept tightly closed. Relaxation was almost impossible. The drunken sailor with a perforated duodenal ulcer was a nightmare for the young surgeon, who could hardly get into the rigid abdomen. He had no relaxation to get in and no relaxation when the time came to close the wound. An incisional hernia was much more frequent than it is today. Mouth operations were a great problem as with an open trachea more blood went down the windpipe than out of the mouth. We cannot thank Ivan Magill, that famous anaesthetist, enough. He was the first man to join the anaesthetic pump directly to the patient's trachea and so we were able for the first time to seal off the area around it completely. We were also able to get the anaesthetist to take up his seat about three feet away and not clutter up the area of the operation.

I remember assisting my chief on one occasion to remove a tongue for a cancer. As soon as the patient was fully anaesthetised he was turned on to his face, the mouth was held fully open with a gag, the table was raised up to its maximum and we both worked from below – rather like a painter painting the ceiling – getting the blood into our own eyes. Sadly, on this occasion the clamp slipped before the vessels were tied and the patient died on the table. My chief was greatly upset; I had never seen him like that before. I had looked on him as a relatively tough chap, but not so. He sat down, and finally some time later he asked me please to drive him home as he did not feel fit to do so himself. I saw him later through several problems as we became very close friends. His first wife had died from an inoperable abdominal cancer; in fact he was sitting down below during the operation when the surgeon called him up to the theatre to show him the open wound and let him see that nothing could be done. I always felt that this was an incredibly cruel thing to do. Many years later when he was very happily remarried his second wife had to have a hysterectomy. I went to see him the night before and found him in tears – I suppose from the memory of his first wife's operation. I rang up the gynaecologist and said I would like to stand by the next day as I would like to offer my blood if blood were needed during the operation. I thought in fact that I would be thanked for this; instead, the gynaecologist, who incidentally was a great friend of mine, said, "My dear chap, what an insult that you should think that I would require blood for a job of that sort." He was quite right as it happened. Many years later my chief himself developed a cancer close to his old gastroenterostomy stoma, an operation which had been done when he was quite a young man by Lord Moynihan and which later he said on many occasions should never have been done.

In the early part of my career I would open the abdomen and he would do the important part of the operation. In the last few months of his life it was the reverse. He made the incision and then sat down, and I went on to finish the job.

It was a very happy friendship which I greatly valued. I was privileged to be trained by a man of that type, a man with good surgical skill but also humanity and integrity.

In the early days prostatectomy had a very high mortality rate. This of course was partly due to the fact that the elderly gentlemen often delayed too long and the kidneys by that time were irretrievably damaged, but the operation itself also had problems such as anaesthesia, bleeding, and sepsis. To overcome the anaesthetic problem my chief used to do the operation as a sort of smash-and-grab raid under ethyl chloride. There were occasions when I was told to stand by with a stop watch. The bladder was well distended, the knife plunged in, and the unfortunate and unsuspecting prostate was rapidly enucleated before it knew what was happening. On one occasion this was all done in 67 seconds but there was sadly still the mopping up and stitching up to be done. It was to some extent a gimmick, and once a decent anaesthesia came in this stopped. The Freyer operation was the standard one for many years: the bladder was left open and drained either on to the abdominal wall or else connected by tube to a bottle at the bedside. Once the urine looked clear and no longer bloodstained, the tube was removed and the wound then slowly closed. As uphill drainage did not seem mechanically sound, for a time a dependent or gravity drain was tried out. This was done from the bladder through the ischiorectal fossa. It had its problems. If the drain was soft rubber the patient sat on it and it did not drain. We then changed this to a metal tube. This was extremely painful as it pressed on the rectum so that method had to be abandoned after a short time. On one occasion we were visited by Hugh Hampton Young of Baltimore, the pioneer of perineal prostatectomy; in fact we were so impressed that the university gave him an honorary degree. After he left us we did two cases using his technique. The first one died and the second did not survive either. It was an awful operation; it was as sensible as coming in through the pantry window to get to the drawing room when the front door was wide open. It was, however, too late then to take back the honorary degree as he was safely back in Baltimore.

My chief himself went to London and had his prostate
dealt with there by Terence Millin who at that time was the
leading expert with the McCarthy resectoscope. Terence
himself later abandoned this operation to popularise the
retropubic approach which we now associate today with his
name.

The modern operation on the prostate gland is a TUR – transurethral resection. The originator is forgotten; he should be remembered; in surgical terms, as far as this problem is concerned it is the greatest thing since the invention of the non-stick pan.

## DISCARDED OPERATIONS

Some operations were discarded because we found that they were based on a misconception; others because, although they were right at the time, later a medical or other form of treatment was found to be of equal value. At one time the enlarged thyroid seemed to have only one method of cure and that was surgery, but with further knowledge of the endocrine glands and their function, some of these cases we found could be dealt with by other means. The same applied to the adrenal, the pituitary, and other endocrine glands. All of this is reasonable, it is progress, and there is no shame attached to it. However, many other operations, when we look back in time through the retrospectoscope, should never have been done. (This instrument is also called "hindsight.")

Radiology did a lot of good but often some harm. A barium meal could show a stomach lying low in the abdomen. The surgeon trained in anatomy and not in physiology was inclined to think that this organ should be in its correct place, so the stupid operation of gastropexy was invented. It made the unfortunate stomach take up a new uncomfortable position in the abdomen that God probably never intended. Sometimes we replaced minor symptoms with a constant dragging pain. One of my senior colleagues after an intussusception always sutured the terminal ileum for the last 6 to 9 inches to the posterior wall, thinking that this might prevent it from telescoping again into the caecum. It must have taken the unfortunate ileum many weeks to wriggle free with its active peristalsis and again lead a normal life.

Radiology again also misled us over the floating or ptosed kidney. The early picture of the renal pelvis which showed us its size and shape was carried out through the bladder – a ureteric catheter was threaded up the ureter and the pelvis of the kidney filled with an opaque fluid. There were two mistakes in these pictures: the first was that the ureter seemed to be straight – of course it did because it had a semi-rigid tube inside it – and secondly one had to guess what was the real size of the kidney pelvis as the operator could make it any size depending on how much fluid he put in, and this might not necessarily be the same as if the pelvis was being filled by normal excretion. With the advent of the intravenous pyelogram (invented by von Lichtenberg) we saw that the ureter often had a kink – of course it had: the kidney was pushed up and down with the rise and fall of the diaphragm and unless it telescoped the ureter must have a kink; but again our anatomical surgeons felt that this was not right, it should be straight – and so an onslaught was made on the unsuspecting kidney; it must be fixed. Many papers were written at that time describing what each man thought was the best method. Some surgeons made a pouch for it on the posterior abdominal wall, others fixed it by a stitch through the kidney substance. The one used by my chief in our unit was to take a strip of the capsule from the back of the kidney. This would be about the size of a broad piece of ribbon, which was hung over and attached to the twelfth rib so that the kidney now was suspended from the twelfth rib like a pair of trousers hanging on a line – a long, troublesome, and useless operation.

There were many other "pexies" carried out, all from the idea that the body had a fixed pattern. We might as well say that everyone should have red hair and blue eyes. In addition to the "pexies" there was another bad operation that got, sadly, much publicity; it was invented by Wilson Hey of Manchester for peptic ulceration. It was badly conceived, with the wrong theoretical background. It was easy to do as it did not entail cutting the viscera. It caused very little trauma but it did a lot of harm. It became popular after a piece of serendipity. A patient was having the blood vessels in his stomach tied in preparation for a gastrectomy. At that moment the anaesthetist was unhappy with the patient's condition and insisted that the operation be stopped and that the abdomen be closed at once. The patient recovered, and after discharge from hospital had no further gastric problems. The ulcer was healed; but was it post hoc ergo propter hoc or not?

Wilson Hey produced the theory that the gastric acidity could be reduced by cutting the major blood vessels as it was along them that the sympathetic fibres were carried, and so the four main gastric vessels were tied. It was a simple operation, it could be done by a junior registrar with his eyes closed, but sadly it was not realised that the idea was quite wrong. It was not the sympathetic but the parasympathetic which was the villain. The operation had a popular phase for a time – too long. Howard Somervel, a very honest man, took the idea to Southern India where there was much peptic ulceration. He did a large series with sadly tragic results.

The vagotomists have now taken over. Leslie Dragstedt, the proponent of vagotomy, had carried out his operation on many hundreds of dogs and had worked out the scientific basis of the operation before he tried it out on men, a very great contrast to Wilson Hey's operation. The vagotomists are now working on a true physiological basis and in time a modus vivendi will be found when a final agreement is reached in the interesting and stimulating fight waged at the moment between the vagotomists on one hand and those who treat with cimetidine and other drugs on the other. I remember doing a vagotomy on the very day that I read about it in the *BMJ*. The patient was a girl of 18, a hairdresser. I remember her well. One does not easily forget one's failures. The operation went well, but she was left with a diarrhoea of some 15 times a day, and this was devastating to her and to myself. It did clear up in time but only after some months. The selective vagotomists have certainly relieved us of that horror.

Attached as I was to a children's hospital, I had to do a great deal of children's surgery and so for the difficult problems such as Hirschsprung's disease and the spastic diplegia we were searching for an answer. I carried out a lumbar sympathectomy for both of these conditions, and today I admit to these with some shame but at that time we were the mirror of what was going on, and one tends to follow the crowd. I did not do a lumbar puncture and a spinal anaesthesia for Hirschsprung's disease. I could see no rationale for that although it was advocated and being done in many centres.

At that time the professor of medicine took ill with some vague form of colitis. It was called "mucus colitis" in those days, whatever that is. It did not respond to any form of treatment and so a very famous man from Harley Street was brought over. He came by train and boat and saw the patient in the morning, operated on him in the afternoon, and got the boat back the same evening. The operation was done under local anaesthesia. It consisted in bringing the appendix to the surface, cutting off its lip, and anchoring it to the surrounding skin. We were now left with a small mucus tube leading directly into the caecum. Each evening one of the professor's colleagues came and put in a catheter and ran in about one pint of a very weak solution. As far as I can remember it was called "albargin," which I think was a colloidal silver preparation. Before leaving, the visiting professor was asked about his fee. He started counting up mileage from London, hours away from the metropolis, what he had lost in hours, etc. He eventually mentioned a figure which at that time seemed astronomical. The patient's brother-in-law was standing by with an open cheque book and a fountain pen at the ready. He did with some trepidation, however, point out before signing the cheque that the professor had now been out of work for two years. Our visitor reduced the fee – somewhat. The professor got well; we never knew whether it was propter or just post hoc.

I was asked several times to operate for high blood pressure, to remove certain of the lower lumbar ganglia or part of the adrenal gland itself. I did this always with some misgiving, but as there was then no alternative it was perhaps allowable. One of the advantages of growing older is to see progress and enjoy it and not be involved in it. We perhaps had to practise the art of surgery – today it is science. I think at times, looking back, that the art had perhaps more fun, and perhaps more tragedy. Science is more serious and certainly much less fun.


## THE RECTUM

The rectum in my day was a very much abused organ. Every form of insult was inflicted upon it. The rectum is trained from birth to be an organ of evacuation, but suddenly the surgeons of my early surgical period were trying to make it a reservoir. The ordinary enema is common sense but then there was a thing called a retention enema, and worse still a nutrient enema; in other words the rectum, which could not see but could only feel, was asked to change its function and way of life. It must have been one of the most uncomfortable treatments that any patient was asked to bear. Many foolish things were put in: for a time, for shock, hot coffee and alcohol – no sense and a great waste of alcohol. To give a nutrient enema, a mixed grill in a liquid form, shows that one has no knowledge of physiology; food is meant to go in at the upper end. The only allowable one was Murphy's drip. This was a high rectal tube; warm fluid such as saline or even just tap water was used. It went in by a drip at much the same rate as an intravenous drip today and it was hoped that absorption would occur at the same rate. This had many advantages. It could be given by a ward nurse or sister, was foolproof, and there was no problem with asepsis. If it succeeded all went well, if not no harm was done.

For a time some experimental work was done on rectal anaesthesia. At first it was ether and olive oil. This had to be passed right into the colon because if it escaped it caused agonising pain in the perineum. I used this on only a very few occasions but its successor Avertin I used for many years, or I should say my anaesthetist used it. He got very intrigued with it and finally actually wrote his MD thesis on it. It was easy to use. The matron would ring the anaesthetist the night before, giving the patient's body weight. The anaesthetist would make up the solution to the right strength and temperature and bring it next day in a thermos flask ready for

94

use. One of my senior colleagues became so impressed with Avertin that he increased the quantity to make it a full general anaesthesia; the drug firm rather disapproved because it was not intended to be used that way, and we all felt it was dangerous as the process was then irreversible. I do not know why it eventually faded out of use because for several years it was very popular and with children a very easy preoperative preparation.

## SPINAL ANAESTHESIA

Spinal anaesthesia I used very much and liked it, but I suppose there was always a slight anxiety about it and so it never had the universal support that one would have expected. I thought when I went to the war and perhaps would have to work single-handed that it might then have been used more extensively, but even then I found it was not too popular. Of course, in a war, evacuation is the one work that dominates in surgery, as it is nice to see the patient safely awake and kicking before he leaves as he is often not going to be seen by the surgeon again.

## REDUNDANT OPERATIONS

I suppose the cure of a disease does produce some nostalgia for the old days. With the medical cure of phthisis what a marvellous selection of operations suddenly became obsolete. Gone was that delightful and delicate operation of phrenic crush or phrenic evulsion. What a pleasure to find a phrenic nerve in the place where it should be. It made one feel that one's anatomical knowledge was really worth while. No longer, however, does the diaphragm need to be paralysed to compress the lower segments of the lung. Gone is the artificial pneumothorax, the cutting of adhesions, pneumo-peritoneum, extrapleural thoracoplasty, or indeed that disfiguring operation of total thoracoplasty with removal of a variable number of ribs.

Sometimes problems arise when we think we are doing the right thing. At one time if the patient – foolishly – was not allowed to get out of bed he was advised to sit up to let the chest move freely. A pillow was put under the buttocks to prevent the patient slipping down the bed, and so he sat up in what was then called the Fowler position, good breathing, yes – but bad venous stasis. How often on the tenth day did we find that swollen and blue left leg with its venous thrombosis, or worse still there was that moment when the patient asked urgently for the bedpan and died from a sudden pulmonary embolus, the clot moving up from the swollen leg. I remember two patients who, doing very well after an operation, both died in the loo. Early ambulation has made all the difference for breathing and the circulation, and the wound heals better, contrary to what was thought at one time. But in my day it must be remembered that wounds were badly sewn up and that a hernia was a very frequent complication.

Early drinking after an operation has also been a great help. No longer even after a gastric operation are we afraid to give small quantities of water. At one time all fluid was forbidden. The result was a dry mouth and rapidly ascending infection into the parotid gland, with a red painful preauricular swelling. This on many occasions had to be opened through the cheek, leaving an ugly scar and sometimes a salivary leak for some time. Early feeding now being the routine, parotiditis is rarely seen today, but I do remember a case. There were two Browns side by side in the ward. One had had a hernia and was ready for home. The other had had a recent gastroenterostomy. The steak and kidney pie was given to the wrong one; it did him no harm at all but the poor chap with a well healed hernia wondered what had gone wrong that he had had to have some sago pudding instead.

Another operation now discarded that I did with no great hope of success – but there was nothing else to offer – was decapulation of the kidney. I did this during the war, on the Gold Coast, for cases of blackwater fever in which the patients died from anuria with great oedema and tension in the kidney. The idea I suppose was that, if we reduced tension, permanent necrosis might not take place. I had no successes in any of my cases. I did a few operations in civil practice after the war at the request of my obstetric colleagues who were faced with the cortical kidney necroses of pregnancy. Again with no success. Dialysis has since taken over and certain patients in whom the kidney has been rested have recovered. Even peritoneal dialysis with its modern modifications can help.

At that time there was also being practised the barbarous operation of removing all the teeth from a patient, doing a complete clearance for what was called, without any scientific basis, "focal sepsis." With the slightest twinge of rheumatism out came the teeth; indeed some people even went further and advocated that they should come out before the rheumatism appeared, even if it was never going to appear. It seems hard to believe today that doctors, and the public alike, were so gullible. Perhaps today some of us are still a little biased in our ideas, which often can be summed up in the phrase that there are two ways of doing a thing: the right way and the way the other chap does it.

Talking of discarded treatments, I must mention Corrigan's button, a treatment for sciatica. I saw it used on two or three occasions by a very senior physician in my own hospital, who kept himself well abreast of anything that was done over 100 years ago. The instrument is a small but thick metal button about the size of the end of one's thumb. It is attached to a metal rod about six inches long, and finally there is a thick wooden handle, which is very important. The patient – male or female – bends forward over a bed or couch. He or she buries the head in a deep pillow. This is very important. The patient cannot see and we hope cannot hear, and when he or she finally yells out in agony the sounds are partially muffled. The patient quickly drops down the pants, with a quick wipe with an iodine swab a hockey-stick-shaped area is marked out to cover, as far as the operator remembers, the outlet of the sciatic nerve from the patient's pelvis and its later descent down the leg. With no word spoken the sister passes the Corrigan's button. It is now almost red hot, having just come off the kitchen stove. The intention is to quickly press the button six or seven times over the line of the sciatic nerve and so produce an enormous counter irritation. The operation is never completed because by the time the red hot button has reached the third or fourth site the patient is off the table and he or she, with or without pants, is halfway down the corridor. The statistics are interesting. There is no follow-up clinic, and there have been no instances of recurrence, as the patients never come back. It is the one treatment for sciatica with 100% success rate.

I was fortunate some years ago to find in the nether regions of the hospital the original Corrigan's button that they had first used in the hospital, and I was able to bring it to a local physicians' club called the Corrigan's Club when they were on a visit to Belfast. It is named after the famous Sir Dominic Corrigan, better or more justifiably known for his famous water hammer or Corrigan's pulse – the sign of aortic incompetence.

Sympathectomy had a tremendous vogue for a short period. Royle's lumbar sympathectomy became very popular; it was easy to do, an attractive piece of surgical anatomical skill which all surgeons enjoy. It got a boost again when George VI had this operation for his intermittent claudication. It still has its uses for increasing the blood supply to the lower limb but sadly for a time it was overused and misused. Lériche's periarterial sympathectomy, where one denuded the femoral artery in the groin of its outer coat which carried the sympathetic fibres, had an extensive trial by us all for a time. In theory it was all right but as the artery is rigid it no longer can react. The same mistake was made by O'Shaughnessy when he attached the omentum with its rich blood supply to the heart muscle in an effort to revascularise a muscle no longer sufficiently fed by the coronary arteries. Unfortunately, O'Shaughnessy did his experimental work on the heart muscle of young greyhounds which of course had a very good blood supply, very different from the fibro-fatty mass of tissue which is so often the case in patients with advanced myocardial failure. I remember one man who saw O'Shaughnessy doing the operation telling me that with the first stitch of the needle into the heart muscle a large piece of fibro-fatty tissue came away. The patient died on the table.

Another useless sympathectomy was the one described by Papin and Ambard who did a Leriche type of operation on the renal artery with the idea that the hydronephrosis that the patient was complaining of was due to imbalance between the sympathetic and the parasympathetic nerve supply. I saw this done on three or four occasions with no success.

## RADIUM NEEDLES AND RADON

For a short time we treated cancer with a barbarous method of putting in radium needles. This was done so that the whole tumour from the centre out would be entirely eradicated. It was used extensively in the tongue and in the breast. Others used it for intestinal tumours. These needles were short, one to two inches long, a sharp point at one end and a hole at the other through which a long piece of linen thread was attached. The needles in actual fact were small hollow tubes carrying the magic material. They were kept when not in use in a heavy leaded box and lent out for the necessary period. It was a painful, septic, disgusting form of treatment especially when used on the tongue.

It was used also quite unscientifically for other types of cases; in fact I saw it being used in my own family circle. My father developed a moderate Dupuytren's contracture of the palmar fascia in his right hand. The modern operation was not then available, so he was asked to carry a plaque containing radium needles strapped to the palm of his hand. He did this for 12 hours daily for five days. The theory was that the contracture was due to young fibroblasts which might be sensitive to radiation. He carried out the treatment loyally but with no effect and, better still, I am glad to say with no bad effects. Radium seeds were used for implanting into brain tumours, etc, and a tube the shape of one's index finger was made to fit into the interior of the uterus to be used for cancer of that organ. This treatment had some success in the metropolis where the tubes were readily available and could be inserted with the radiation at full strength, but in Belfast with no air transport it raised many problems.

Today this all seems very primitive when we see what modern surgery can do. Though I am no longer able to play the game on the field, I still enjoy it from the touchline.

# A guinea's worth

Recently in London I saw a golden guinea for sale for £350 and it reminded me of the only occasion when I was ever paid a guinea for my medical services. The patient had varicose veins and was due to have an injection. When told it would be three guineas – the price for the job at that time, so it shows how long ago it was – he replied, "You doctors talk of guineas and many of you have never seen one." I told him that I had seen one but sadly did not possess one. "Right," he said; "on Tuesday I will pay you in a guinea: today's value for one is £2.10 shillings, so I will pay you one guinea, one ten shilling note, and three single shillings." This he duly did. I did not know then that he was a well known numismatist, and although I suggested that he might repeat the process on a subsequent visit, sadly he paid me in the contemporary currencies of the realm.

So my mini fee so long ago for varicose veins injection has now taken on a new value; I suppose it is in keeping with what is charged today for the same job.

My father often quoted an old tag for me:

A guinea it will sink, and a pound it will float,
But I'd rather have a guinea than a one pound note.

*If this was true in 1800 (George III), when the last guinea was minted, it is more than ever true today. My spade guinea (so called because on the reverse is a design like the ace of spades) still remains safely away in the bank, I hope.*

# Instrumental pieces

Many changes have taken place over the past few years in the sale of drugs and instruments. In the old days a young surgeon like myself had to have a fully equipped operating kit, a bag of instruments, a method of sterilising, and a drum for the soft goods such as towels, gowns, masks, and gloves. The instruments were gradually collected; often the basis was second-hand ones passed on possibly by your chief or from a retired senior surgeon. You supplemented these as soon as you financially could do it. I started with the cheapest form of artery forceps; they were chromium-plated, light, and when new very satisfactory, but the plating came off very easily and when bits of this were left in the wound I am sure, although they did no harm, they were not pleasant from an aesthetic point of view. I remember well a representative calling from one of the large firms. Thackery and Downes sent travellers round regularly; this particular representative had been told that I was now doing better and perhaps I could afford some stainless steel instruments. From then on with each visit I gradually replaced the old ones. At the same time they asked if I needed any silkworm gut or catgut which, of course, we had to buy at regular intervals. Silkworm gut, not used now, came in limited lengths because the parotid gland of the unfortunate silkworm could produce only a limited amount. It came in various colours and thicknesses: thick, thin, and medium. It was hard to tie and not very pliable. Catgut we either got raw in hanks which had to be sterilised by boiling in an iodine solution (the container was kept on the boil over the kitchen stove for a certain length of time; this was the six-day catgut for tying small vessels) or the longer lasting catgut came in glass tubes. It was genuine gut, not from the cat but from the small intestine of, often, a lamb. New Zealand at that time was sending masses of frozen lamb to the United Kingdom; the flesh was eaten and the entrails came in frozen packs and were processed in Britain. One very popular brand at that time was that of the London Hospital Catgut Company.

Throwaway instruments did not exist. I still find them somewhat hard to accept. My family doctor comes to give me my annual anti-flu injection. I do not think it does me any good but I allow him to go through the motions. Having dealt with me, he throws away syringe, needles, etc, and takes a new set for my wife. In the old days I would have done the whole family with the same needle and kept it for another occasion. Perhaps as a Scottish Presbyterian, or perhaps because I was brought up through the rigours of the first world war, I find that sometimes this waste is hard to accept. I saw a surgeon recently opening a pack of two sterile gloves to do a rectal examination. Both gloves, including the unused one, were then thrown into the dustbin. The sharp instruments, scalpels and so on, had to be sharpened regularly in my time. I would take a large collection of them to a retired police constable, who also did all the work for our main hospitals.

The surgeon at that time had to have a full kit of operating instruments as so much work was done in private homes as well as in nursing homes not fully equipped. Some surgeons in fact were perhaps better equipped than the hospital in which they worked. My old chief always brought his own cystoscopes on his operating day, with four boxes under his arm like a tennis player arriving at Wimbledon. He also had a diathermy apparatus which he kept at home. This was called officially a portable diathermy, but those of us responsible for carrying it to the ward were inclined to call it "shiftable." We finally learnt to transport it on a trolley. My chief, as I said, used it at home in his own consulting room where he did a lot of cystoscopy work. He had a water container which, when pulled up to the ceiling by rope and pulley, gave a good head of pressure with which to fill the bladder. This on one occasion was in full flow when he was called to the telephone; he returned rapidly in response to frantic shrieks and shouts from the patient as the bladder had now reached almost bursting point. It was really not a very scientific piece of technology.

My first cystoscope I bought on a visit to Germany. It was a Wolf Shindler, the best that was on the market. It cost £16, but when I said I lived in Belfast the salesman said this was rather sad because there was 50% import tax into the United Kingdom, making it £24. He said it was unfortunate that I did not live in Dublin which was tax free, so I decided that I did live in Dublin and gave my address as c/o Royal College of Surgeons in Ireland. To get it from Dublin I thought would be quite easy. Some weeks later my house surgeon, playing rugby for the university and, incidentally, an Irish international, said he was going down to Dublin to play against Trinity College. He agreed to bring the box back. There would be no difficulty about this; he would put it into his bag among his dirty togs. The train was never searched on a Saturday night. Alas, the post-match party went on too long, they missed the train, and instead of coming back on a Saturday night in a crowded and rowdy train they came back home on Sunday morning in an empty one. Poor John, who had no fear on the rugby field, suddenly got the wind up about my cystoscope. He went along the entire corridor until he found an empty first class carriage, and he put the cystoscope under the seat. When he collected it in Belfast it was almost red hot as it had been sitting on the hot pipes; in fact it was still hot when he delivered it to me some hours later, but I am glad to say it was in good working order.

The Bayer Company's representative was a regular visitor. On one occasion he asked me if there was any likelihood of my being near Cologne as his firm would be delighted to see me. I told him that my wife and I were going in fact to be two days in Cologne later on our way somewhere else. He said I was to ring the firm and contact a certain person who would be expecting me. I duly rang up the firm and they said they would send a car next morning. They assumed that I was part of a group of visitors from Ireland. When I got there I found that, purely by accident, our visit did coincide with a small party from Dublin. I did not know any of them as they were mostly in the Public Health Service, but they included the Minister of Health, whom I had met. We had a very interesting morning; they were producing gallons of a red fluid which I had not heard of. It was called Prontosil and it had the advantage of curing you of your infection but it also had the disadvantage that you turned bright red like a lobster. However, with further experimentation they were able to remove the red dye and produce the famous sulphonilamide, but even that in its early stages had disadvantages: one had to avoid salts, onions, and eggs, but again with research these disadvantages were overcome.

We had a magnificent lunch. I remember in the large room one enormous side table covered with all varieties of alcoholic drinks, and on the other side a table with the largest selection of non-alcoholic drinks I have ever seen. We sat down to lunch, 20 or so, at a long table with a magnificent bowl of roses in the middle of the table. At the end of the meal our German host made us welcome in a most felicitous speech. When he had sat down we looked round, feeling that one of the Irish party should get up and thank him. Finally one of the senior Dublin visitors got up and in an impromptu speech thanked the hosts. Before we left the German came to our Dublin friend and said he was sure that he would like to take his speech home with him. My friend was completely taken aback and said he had really made no speech, just a word of thanks. However, to cut a long story short, the German host then presented him with a rubber disc on which he could play back his speech. It seems that there was a microphone in the middle of the rose bowl relayed to the office next door.

As they were showing us round I asked if there was any difficulty with security. My guide said that in that large room there were 400 true research scientists working year in and year out, some of them of course with no results, but of that 400 four were spies employed to see that if a real discovery was made, like aspirin, it would not be made available to another firm. In fact, on one occasion they had found one man in the process of doing this. They also told me another interesting story. It concerned the visit of three Japanese doctors. They were shown all over the building, and it was noticed that one of the men never took his hand out of his pocket. They looked at him carefully and then decided that the elegant button on his coat was, in fact, the lens of a camera. In a case like this you can do one of two things: you can be nasty and ask him to take off his coat; or you can be very kind and offer to show him even more of the factory. This they did. They took him all over the factory, and finally down to the deep $x$ ray department. When our Japanese friend was suitably placed they showed him how the machine worked by switching the current on. Any film that he had in the camera and in his pockets, I am afraid, was all destroyed; there was no unpleasantness, and it was equally effective.

Surgeons by and large are great collectors of instruments. Often they have seen a job well done and they are inclined to think that it is due to the tools and forget that it is really due to the man in charge. Most surgeons who went to Paris, for instance, came home with a Reverdin's needle which the French used so dextrously, but we tend to forget that they had to use this as their gloves at that time were so thick they prevented them from having any finger tip feeling. I still have a rusty Reverdin's needle in a cupboard somewhere. I have seen the French use this famous needle for intestinal anastomosis, then they have sewn up the abdominal wall, and finally with a cutting needle they have been able to close the skin with ease; all this done with great speed. I remember also seeing them doing with great skill a hare lip and cleft palate, but even with the French I think the Reverdin needle has now been displaced. When the Americans came in hordes to see Arbuthnot Lane doing his magnificent bone work using his famous "no touch technique" they all crossed the road from Guy's Hospital to Downes' Instrument Shop and went back home with several hundred pounds' worth of instruments. I wonder if they were satisfactory. They were enormously long, and very heavy – the length did keep people at a distance – but Arbuthnot Lane was a very strong man and did not mind the weight. A very great contrast to Moynihan, whose instruments were so very light and he himself had a very gentle touch. Arbuthnot Lane in his later years became quite a crank. He had a theory that almost all illnesses were due to large bowel stasis and absorption of toxic products. He nearly went so far as to suggest that lesions, even such as a brain tumour, might be caused by this problem. So he popularised the operation of total colectomy. With no large bowel the patient who had had slight constipation was now left with an uncontrollable diarrhoea. Lane refused to recant or withdraw his ideas, and finally, being an honest man, he felt he could not write to the press if he was still a doctor, so he resigned from the medical profession. It is said that a boy from Paris was sent to Lane with an ununited fracture of the tibia for plating or other orthopaedic correction, but by this stage Lane had taken up his colostomy idea and suggested removal of the colon rather than plating the boy's tibia. I think the boy went back to Paris without any treatment – I hope so.

Some surgeons seem to specialise in complicated instruments. This was particularly so in those early operations for opening the skull. Also there were masses of heavy gastrectomy clamps. What a contrast it is today when suturing is replaced by metal clips and one closure of a pair of blades. The Russian clamp for resection of oesophagus and rectum, etc certainly saves much time and seems to be just as efficient. I saw this first used in Russia in 1957 when they did a carotid artery anastomosis on a dog. The artery was cut across, joined up at once with a clamp and staples, and the dog was able to walk away in a few minutes. In some ways it is sad that anonymity has replaced eponymity. At one time, when wooden splints were in great use, each splint was named after a surgical master. The Thomas's splint still remains but Colles's splint, the long Liston and so on have all been forgotten. This happened more or less with the arrival of plaster of Paris when the splint was made to fit the fracture and not the fracture made to fit into the shape of the splint. Pannet's double-bladed forceps were in regular use in my day. They held both sides of the peritoneum together when there was much tension with a rigid and struggling patient, but with curare and complete relaxation this elegant instrument has now become obsolete.

On the anaesthetist's table there was always a barbarous instrument called the tongue forceps. This was used to pull the tongue forward if it fell back and obstructed the airway. It was a flat-faced instrument which crushed the tongue and left it swollen and painful for several days. With the invention of the intratracheal tube this all disappeared overnight.

Metal plates took a long time to be accepted. Sepsis naturally was one problem, but we also had to get a metal with no electrolytic properties. It took a long time to get a suitable plastic material for the head or socket of the hip for hip replacement, and only recently has the implant of a new lens into the eye after removal of a cataract become satisfactory, as for many years the eye acidity caused changes in the early implants. We indeed have had much help from our biomedical friends.

# Put to the test

Examinations are really a very poor test of a person's general ability. They can test his memory but not his personality, his integrity, or his technical skill. They can also be unfair since the examiner – thank goodness – is not a computer; he can be fallible. How can the pretty girl fail to make a better initial impression on a susceptible examiner than her spotty-faced, untidy competitor? Surely the young man with a few international rugby caps in his pocket starts with a definite bonus – and rightly so.

In examinations there is luck – serendipity, timing, call it what you will. I remember going in for my viva for my final MB. It was 4 30 or so in the afternoon. I was preceded by a waitress bearing a tray with a pot of tea and the delightful aroma of fresh buttered scones. The examiners' faces lit up, but the light soon became extinguished when they saw that I was following closely behind. I could just hear our local professor saying to the eminent extern examiner, "Sir James, do you take one lump or two?" I then saw a small piece of paper being passed, and although I could not read it I felt it said, "This boy is all right so one question might be enough." So I was asked why measles killed more children each year than all the other diseases of children added together. I was able to answer it and so got my MB and they continued to enjoy their tea and hot buttered scones.

I remember tea arriving on another occasion. It was my final for the fellowship in London. I was ushered behind the screens to examine a young woman. At the same moment a tray of tea and biscuits was put down in front of her. She was very polite but very definite.

I was able to answer it and so got my MB

"Sir, I have been examined so often this afternoon that I insist on having my tea now if you don't mind."

I explained to her that this was the most important moment of my life and that the tea was really a secondary consideration.

She said, "I will answer any questions but will not be examined," and so for 20 minutes I had the best lecture, a real critique on cervical rib, better than I have ever had from any professor. She told me that most of the candidates had missed the fact that she had one on the other side. She gave the differential diagnosis, she repeated to me all that had been said by the previous candidates and the questions of the examiner; in fact I had a splendid time, and so when the final laying-on of hands took place she did not need to do the full striptease that she had done so often for my predecessors. So thanks to some Indian tea and a cooperative lady I got my fellowship. (The overseas candidates in those days were always taken on the first day. This, it was said, was done to allow them to get back home and start working for their next attempt, as it was assumed that most of them failed.)

One's colleagues can occasionally have a perverted sense of humour at such times. Going up the steps on that same day I met another candidate, a great friend and later a man who put his own name to a certain prostatectomy. He asked me if I knew the freezing point of urine. I had never thought that urine could freeze. I had heard of many ladies who had said that they had been passing "scalding urine" but freezing urine was something I had never considered. This, he said, was a question that we were bound to be asked. There also were those others who came along when you were well tensed up and told you that if you did not know the number of chromosomes in a queen bee then you might as well retire. All very funny, many years later, but not so amusing at the time.

There is a great technique in being an examinee as well as an examiner. To be stupid is bad, but to be too clever is worse. The story is told of a candidate who was given a Dupuytren's contracture of the palmar fascia as his major case. He diagnosed it in one and a half minutes flat, but still

20 minutes remained. How could he fill this time? He was not the sort of chap who could sit back and do nothing, so he went to the tray with all the instruments of torture. He started with a stethoscope and gave the patient the once over fore and aft, then blood pressure. He then saw a patellar hammer, a tuning fork – did a Rhomberg's test, then sensation with pin and cotton wool, and then a quick look at the discs. There were still eight minutes to go so he went back to the tray and he saw a rubber glove – why not? It took some explanation but the patient finally submitted and agreed to have a rectal examination – indeed, had it been a lady he would have done a cervical smear for good measure. He was that sort of chap. But lo and behold, on rectal examination he found that the patient had indeed an early – symptomless as yet – cancer of the rectum. This was a bit of serendipity. At last the curtains opened and the examiners appeared.

"Well, young man, if untreated what is the final state of the patient?" (for fear you have forgotten by now, the patient had a Dupuytren's contracture).

"Well, Sir, probably liver secondaries and jaundice, etc."

The balloon went up, the examiner was not amused; the candidate could be too clever – but he did get through.

Humble examiners do exist. The story is told of the bright young man who, facing across the narrow table, could see the mark sheet easily between the bottles. After each question he saw the elderly examiner putting down "six." When the bell rang the candidate said, "Sir, I hope I have satisfied you," to which the examiner said, "You have indeed done very well." The candidate then said, "I could not avoid seeing that you put down a 'six' each time; is that six out of six?"

"No," said the examiner "that is six out of ten. You see, I am only seven out of ten myself, and as yet you do not know quite as much as I do."

An eccentric examiner can be a bit of a problem at times. I remember a well known London physician, with a large textbook to his credit, coming as an extern examiner to Belfast. Staying with the local professor, he insisted that all ticking clocks should be stopped. This was unfortunate as the professor had three grandfather clocks which were his pride and joy and which were never allowed to be stopped; in fact it was almost like going to stay with someone and asking them to drown their favourite cat just because you cannot stand cats. His other insistence was that his bed must lie directly north to south – or east to west, I forget now which it was. His host naturally did not know north from south – who does? – but this caused no problem as the visitor had brought his own compass and he was told to do anything he wished as long as he put things back to the normal position before leaving.

Examinations are certainly a battle of wits or gamesmanship. Later, when I became an examiner, I saw the problem from the other side of the table. In Dublin on one occasion I saw a very pretty girl appearing. There were three of us examining together. When she reached the first examiner – a local surgeon well known for his surgical expertise – she said, "I will never forget that wonderful operation you did late one night on that frail old woman with an intestinal obstruction – no one ever thought she would live, etc, etc." Then on to the next examiner – a Dublin surgeon more notable as a writer and an historian. "Sir," she said, "I will never forget that wonderful lecture you gave on cleft palate, I was able to repeat it word for word to my mother when I got home, etc, etc." Finally she came up to me whom she had never seen or heard of before. What would the technique be? In a very confidential voice she said, "Sir, I thought your two questions on the paper were the fairest I have seen for several years, but I am very ashamed that I did not answer them as well as I should have done," but coming closer and more confidentially she said, "I must explain, Sir, that my period had come on that morning." So even PMT can help in the final examination; and it did.

In England on one occasion I had trouble that I had never had before and it caused me at the time great embarrassment. I had an insoluble difference of opinion with my opposite number. I insisted on giving the candidate 0 out of 20; he wanted to give him 10 out of 20, and this I refused. The patient was a woman with an advanced cancer of the breast.

It was very unfortunate that a hint had been given to the students and they were told that there was a simple lump in the breast which slipped through one's fingers like the soap in a bath, with no retraction of nipple or any other signs. There was in fact such a case but by accident a woman with advanced cancer of the breast at that moment had come to the outpatients department, and so the surgeon in charge, seeing hers was a suitable case, sent her straight along to the examination hall. There was a hard mass, fixed, with nipple retraction, and palpable glands, but my candidate insisted on sticking to the "hint". I finally said to my co-examiner that as we were so far apart in our marks the candidate in fairness should be referred to another pair of examiners. This was done. I found out later that the candidate was distantly related to my co-examiner.

The time of day can alter the marks. In England a very good lunch can make the examiners see things through rosy spectacles and, indeed, they have been known to fall asleep. This raises with the candidate a great problem. Should you waken the examiner, and if you do will he be cross and ashamed, and so fail you? One is always inclined to take it out of the other person if one is in the wrong. The old aphorism is so true: "They ne'er forgive who *do* the wrong". Some candidates think it is best to let the examiner sleep and be wakened by the bell. If he is a clever examiner he does not wake with a start. He opens his eyes slowly and says, "That is very good indeed," and gives the candidate a pass mark. Naturally you cannot award honours if you were asleep.

I said that in England the candidates do better after lunch, but it happens even earlier than that in Ireland, particularly the south of Ireland, because at 11 am, halfway through the morning session, in hospitals controlled by the nuns the coffee is quite exceptional – half coffee and half Irish whiskey; and for those visitors who, like myself, do not have this normally at home at that time it has a wonderfully softening effect on the nerves and the temper. It is much easier to get honours in your degree after coffee time.

In Belfast one year I was one of the junior surgical examiners. A certain Irish rugby international was up for his final MB. In the morning one of the senior physicians, himself a former notable international with many Irish caps, spoke to me and pointed out that if I failed "so and so" I should certainly have to leave the town. It is true that the candidate had spent more time at the base of the scrum than at the bedside. A story is told about me on this occasion which is entirely untrue. It is said that I gave him a rubber tube and said that this could be used for bladder operations and that the first two letters were "c" and "a". It is said that for fear he might say "caliper" I quickly told him that the third letter was "t" and when he guessed catheter I passed him at once. I wish to say that this is an exaggeration: I did show him a catheter and he got the answer first shot, and so he did get through.

Examining in some areas can be a problem. In one hospital not only did the candidates recognise the specimen but could also recognise the person. The story is told that when shown a cancer of the breast in a bottle the candidate was able to say not only what it was but that it belonged to Mrs McGuinness the local publican's wife, who was still alive and well. In the same hospital a well known London surgeon – later PRCS – got very bad marks when he came to examine there and had the audacity and unfairness to bring with him from London an envelope full of his own x rays, and use these instead of the x rays in the department which had been used over and over again for the past 10 or 15 years. The examiner had always kept them in a drawer for this purpose. The students felt that this was indeed very unfair. On my first visit to one area as a very young and too eager examiner I said, after a very good dinner, to the professor with whom I was staying that I would like to go down to the hospital – not far away – and have a look at the cases. He was very unwilling for me to do this. He pointed out that it was unusual, but finally agreed. I found on arrival, however, that all the candidates for the next day were there and already doing a practice run over the course. I soon saw why the professor rather disapproved.

I remember another incident when, on a very very hot June day with the windows in the ward wide open and the examiners in their shirtsleeves, an attractive (semi-attractive) young lady arrived for the examination with a large handbag and wearing a full length waterproof. I suggested that the bag should be left on the table and that she would be happier and more comfortable without her waterproof, but she refused and nothing could be done about it. Examiners have no power to make lady candidates undress. However, it was soon seen when she got behind the screen that in the inside pockets of the waterproof she had a regular library of books. Fortunately she was a poor candidate and really failed herself, so there was no need to make a fuss.

It is always much more pleasant to examine away from one's own hospital; it is more relaxing since you have not the responsibility of examining your colleagues' children, whom you do not want to fail. I was for many years extern examiner to a university in the Midlands. The professor and I had been longstanding friends, a friendship which had started when we were together in Cairo during the war. He was a somewhat eccentric professor – an understatement. In Cairo we often went together to the souk, where he went to the carpet shops. Many carpets were rolled out for his inspection while he and I sat sipping Turkish coffee. Having found no carpet to his liking, he politely excused himself and we went to another shop further down where a similar scene took place. When we had visited the fourth shop, I asked him if he really wanted to buy a carpet. He said not at all but he liked Turkish coffee. I am sure the local shopkeepers knew him well as he did this frequently. When asked by him after the war to be an extern examiner I accepted with alacrity; he was now professor of surgery. I said he was unusual, but I was to find out more. He lived in a large double-fronted house near the university. There were two large bedrooms on the first floor with bay windows. He slept in one and the one on the other side was the visitors' room and was obviously for me. When I went in I found there was a double door, and linoleum on the floor. I soon found that the usual inhabitant of that room was his monkey. He had had two at one time, a male and a female, but by the time I was there one had died and the other was now getting quite elderly. I found that for the four days of my visit he took the monkey into his room, in fact into his own bed with him, but on the last night of my visit to him I found that the monkey had got troublesome in the middle of the night and the professor, poor chap, found it was easier to leave it alone and for him to go downstairs and sleep on the settee in the kitchen – a poor preparation for a full day's examination. He was a splendid fellow; a loyal friend to all, including the monkey.

The story is told, I am not sure if it is apocryphal or not, that a senior member of the council of the Royal College of Surgeons who was examining in the fellowship one year mingled with the "walking wounded" outpatients who were kindly allowing themselves to be used as examination material. The examiner in question had a slight limp; this indeed was part of his personality, just as Churchill's cigar or Chamberlain's monocle were. This examiner, when about to enter the examination hall, was approached by one of the candidates who said to him, "I see you are going to the examination, and I do see you have a limp. Is it your foot, knee, or ankle?"

The examiner in a quiet voice replied, "It is an old TB knee and I have had it since I was a child."

The candidate was well satisfied and passed him a 10 shilling note. Twenty minutes later the candidate was somewhat discomfited when taken to a table for his viva to find the unknown man was his examiner. The examiner recognised him, gave him a viva on TB knee, told him that he had done very well indeed and, in fact, handed him his 10 shilling note back. At Sir Harry Platt's 100th birthday dinner I meant to ask him if this was true, but there was no time for such trivialities – there were 350 in all at the dinner and after Harry had shaken hands with 175 men and had been kissed by 175 ladies there was little time left for me to put my important question to him.

# Bribery and corruption

Just after the second world war I was asked to be external examiner in surgery at the National University of Ireland with the examination starting in Cork. No coal being available, the trains were travelling on peat, wood, in fact any combustible material. It took one day from Belfast to Dublin and another from Dublin to Cork, with many stops.

On the way to Dublin, while talking to a friend, I told him I was catching the 9 am train the next day to Cork. He said, "That is what you think; it is the only train in the day and it is full from 7 am so you will find no seats available. But I can tell you what to do. You must ask for Johnnie MacLaughlin with a £1 note – just visible in your hand – and he will help you."

Being a man opposed, in theory, to bribery and corruption, I decided that I would be at the station myself at 7 am. This I did and found a very crowded platform. I went forward to the sharp end of the train and then back to the blunt end and indeed saw that all the carriages were entirely full. Pocketing my pride and my morals, I hailed a junior porter – I would say a young man of house surgeon or junior registrar status – and asked him if he could possibly find Mr Johnnie MacLaughlin, who I assumed was the consultant railway porter in charge. Johnnie appeared in due course. I explained that I had been told that he could get me a seat. I made the £1 a little more obvious but not ostentatiously so. He said, "Hold your ground" and proceeded to go forward to the front end of the train and then to the back. He then reported to me that the train was full. This from my own "recce" I already knew. He thought for a moment and then said, "Could you have a limp?"

I had never been asked that before, but I said I could try; so he proceeded to walk very slowly up the platform to the front of the train carrying my bag, and I walked slowly behind him with a minor limp. I still, after 40 years, feel very ashamed. At the second carriage from the front there was a "RED CROSS" on the window and a notice which said,

"For the wounded." He opened the door, lifted my bag carefully on to the rack, helped me in, and after the £1 note had changed hands he quietly closed the door and departed.

After a short time I recovered and in a truly professional manner leant over to my colleague on the opposite seat. I said, "My good chap, what happened to you?" To which he replied, "Exactly the same as happened to you." This made my conscience somewhat easier – at least for the time being. I found later that all the occupants had had the same experience. I am astonished that no intelligent chap noticed that these same unfortunate limpers left the platform in Cork with a brisk and manly step.

# Roundabout

## THE WHEEL COMES FULL CIRCLE

*Surgical clubs – visiting around Europe and Russia –
Gonzalez the Good to moping monkeys – surgeons in
retirement – clocks, stamps, and clean banknotes*

# Fellows travelling

A special feature of British surgery is the small surgical club. This exists to a much lesser extent on the Continent and even in America. Started originally by Lord Moynihan, who felt that the provincial surgeons were at a disadvantage compared with their London counterparts who were able to make daily contacts, the clubs by their overseas visits enabled members to keep up the friendships with continental surgeons that they had made in the first world war. The size of the club was as a rule restricted to about 25 members. It was said originally that this allowed eight people in the operating theatre to see the surgeons at work at three operating tables and it meant also that when wives joined their husbands on an overseas visit the numbers were not too large. In his history of one of these clubs Charles Wells says, "New members have been recruited over the years, but there is an unwritten rule that they should be amiable, enthusiastic, interested, interesting, intelligent, and above all friendly and clubbable, with a sense of humour. These are the best ingredients for a happy club."

On these visits, particularly on the overseas visits, we had many exciting experiences. My first visit with my own club was to Vienna and Budapest. The year was 1938, and that is important. My wife and I had a luxurious journey out on the Golden Arrow to Vienna for £23 – I forget now whether that was for one or both. It is absurd when we think of that figure today. We arrived at our hotel on the Ringstrasse in the afternoon, we unloaded our clothes into the various drawers and cupboards and had, with the others, a very happy evening and dinner. Next morning the men all left at 8 am for the Allgemeine Krankenhaus where we had a very interesting operating session, seeing Denk and Rantzi and others at work. One, if not both, of these two men was liquidated later. Rantzi was, I think, a relative of von Eiselsberg. On getting back in the late afternoon to my hotel, I was met by the hotel porter who was considerably embarrassed and told me that he had moved us both and, in fact, all the party, into another hotel. He said it was equally good and I would find our clothes all laid out for us. I protested and said I had booked in six months previously and my clothes were hanging up in the various cupboards. However, there was nothing we could do; we went to the other hotel, equally good, our clothes we found indeed had been hung up and laid out in the various drawers. Next day we found the reason when we read in the paper that von Papen, Hitler's envoy, had arrived and had taken over the Hotel Bristol lock, stock and barrel. There was nothing that anyone could do about it. This was 1938 – it was the beginning of the Anschluss – my first experience of total irresistible power.

We saw Böhler, who showed us his successes but we were told he also had a chamber of horrors which was not on view to visitors. He showed us his technique with the compression fracture of the spine where he had the patient up and walking about in two or three days. We also saw Finsterer. By contrast he worked in a miserable theatre and was clearly not a member of the "establishment". He spoke good English and gave us a welcome, whereas the reception from Denk and Rantzi had been very lukewarm.

We were amused to see in the shop attached to the hospital photographs of the surgeons whom we had seen working. We were obviously expected to buy them, which we did, and I still have mine signed by the great men of that time. This is a custom that has not yet come into our British hospitals, thank goodness.

Böhler we rather disliked for his arrogance, his self-assurance and perhaps for his politics. He did however, impress some people. The story is told of a young Englishman who returned to sit an orthopaedic examination in England, having had a spell with Böhler. When asked by the examiner how he would treat a fracture near the ankle he at once said he would use the Böhler fixation splint; with a fracture of the tibia it was the Böhler extension splint, with the femur another Böhler splint, and so on for hip and spine. He never gave a reason or a sensible answer. The examiner could stand this no longer. Finally he said to the student that he supposed for a fracture of the skull the candidate would fit the patient with a Böhler hat.

From Vienna we went down to Budapest. There were many different methods of doing this journey – fast train, slow train, by air one hour, by bus five hours, or by Danube steamer. This latter took 12 hours; it sounded attractive, but was long, tedious, and became rather cold. We went by bus, stopping in every small town where we were able to get out and visit the markets and places of interest. In Budapest we met von Lichtenberg, the inventor of the intravenous pyelogram (Uroselectan). As a Jew he had been chased out of Germany and had taken refuge in Budapest and now with the Anschluss he saw the same was going to happen again; in fact not long afterwards he fled to South America. He had become a very rich man. His theatre was most impressive, rather like a cave – black walls, no windows, but ideal for endoscopy and very impressive when the lights came on. Another surgeon doing magnificent work was Professor von Bakay; he, we were told, mysteriously disappeared later.

In retrospect we should have noticed the general air of depression. The Austro-Hungarian Empire had lost so much of its surrounding country that it was said that Vienna was like a man with a head but no body. One very large insurance company with headquarters in Vienna, with the loss of so much territory no longer required its full quota of offices, and so it converted the upper floors into a casualty department, putting Böhler in charge; in fact the casualty off the street could be taken directly by an ambulance into a lift and carried to the upper floor. This was good business; the patient got good care, and the insurance company had less to pay. It was almost as if in London the ambulance was to enter the Prudential Building in Holborn and be taken by lift to the top floor.

Each visit brings back very personal memories. I still think with astonishment of an operation that I saw in Switzerland. The patient had an advanced cancer of the breast. On the theatre floor was a brazier filled with charcoal. To supply the necessary oxygen in the theatre there was close by a ladies' electric hair dryer which blew in the required air. In the brazier were four or five large soldering irons each with a large metal head, a long shaft, and a wooden handle. A shuttle service provided the surgeon with a red hot soldering iron. This was pressed on the breast and finally the whole area was completely destroyed leaving a large black dead mass of tissue. This, it was said, would slough off in a few days and as soon as a clean granulating surface appeared it would be covered with a skin graft. The theory behind this barbarous technique was that not only did we destroy the lump and the breast itself but we also coagulated all the entire drainage area, whether that be towards the axilla, the liver, or to the intercostals through the chest wall. I have never seen this done before or since, I am glad to say. What a contrast to the technique of today when cancer of the breast is being treated by minor or minimal destructive surgery.

In Spain all members of our club remember well a certain operation. It was a partial gastrectomy. We went into the theatre and, having taken our seats, saw a young man in his 20s walk in. He took off his shirt, dropped his trousers down, took off his slippers, and lay naked on the operating table. A nursing sister dressed as a nun approached him with a razor – a dangerous sight – and dealt with his suprapubic area. Next, a screen was put up to block his view of the operation and a further nun was put in charge of his head. She had a fan. When opened this was to give him some fresh air, but when closed she would give him a brisk tap on the forehead and remind him how lucky he was to have as his surgeon the famous Gonzales Bueno. We called him "Gonzales the Good". She also pointed out to the patient that he should appreciate that he was being watched by so many eminent surgeon visitors, all of which may have impressed him but did not ease the pain as the whole gastric operation was being carried out under a local anaesthetic with him being conscious throughout. The surgeon, a large man, entered wearing a long towelling dressing gown, with a label on his chest which told us that he was indeed Gonzales Bueno. The operation had no special feature; it was more a pylorectomy than a partial gastrectomy. Finally the wound was closed in one layer by through-and-through wire sutures. These were twisted and cut short so that the wound looked, and I suppose also felt, like a piece of barbed wire. We waited for a trolley to come and take the patient back to bed, but no, in came his shirt, trousers and slippers and he walked out of the theatre. Several of us went to see him afterwards expecting to see him at last in bed, but he was sitting in a chair as the surgeon said his diaphragm and breathing worked better when he was sitting up. We felt his pulse, and I certainly would have put his head down as he was now certainly quite shocked.

The name "Gonzales the Good" of course intrigued us; we tried to think of British counterparts. What about Dickie the Right or Lawrence the Able? Sir Stanford Cade was one of our party and was one of the first to suggest, "What about Stanford the Cad?" There can be much fun on such occasions.

Our visit to Padua coincided with the centenary of Bassini's birth, so a hernia operation using the original technique invented by that great man was performed. Some time after that Heneage Ogilvie, who was the leader and founder of our own club, produced one of many aphorisms when he said that all bad things in surgery began with "B" – Bassini, Billroth, and Battle (the incision). He was safe enough with the first two, who were both long dead, but Battle's son Dickie, a renowned plastic surgeon, far from dead, confronted Heneage later about this and he told me many years later that he finally got a minor apology.

On a visit to France I saw for the first time people wearing two masks, one to hold the moustache and beard in check and the other to cover the face. Things have changed much since then. On another occasion I went to Paris to take a special course in genitourinary surgery. It lasted two weeks and cost £30. It took place at L'Hôpital Necker under a famous urologist, Legue. The course consisted of lectures and operations, plus a session in the dissecting room where we each carried out operations on the dead body. I was astonished on the first day to have a complete cadaver allotted to myself, on which I did the routine kidney, ureter, and bladder operations. In the operating theatre I saw a prostatectomy done under local anaesthesia for the first time. Another operation which we found rather horrifying, but which I later found was a regular showpiece of this particular surgeon, was a nephrectomy. After the surgeon had brought the kidney out, he removed it with the clamp still on but the pedicle not yet tied. He then proceeded to open the clamp, and a fountain of blood straight from the aorta gushed out.

"Gentlemen," he said, "this can happen to any one of you, and I will show you what to do."

He then quickly packed the wound tightly, waited for a short time and then, slowly putting in a finger, he worked down from the top of the wound, putting on clamp after clamp somewhere in the region of the renal pedicle. Finally he removed the pack; the wound was dry, but the patient had suffered much blood loss. I now wondered how he was going to tie these 15 or more forceps, but not so. These were left in situ, the skin was closed over them with the handles sticking out, and in a few days he said he would start to remove them one by one, taking several days to remove them all, taking perhaps one or two forceps off each day. We were all rather horrified, particularly as in this case the patient was a young man of 20 or so with an advanced tuberculous kidney. We questioned among ourselves greatly the ethical basis for doing it. I have told this story to many people and I have been astonished to find how many others had seen this same man doing this same thing. It was obviously his party piece.

Foreign clubs did not often visit Britain. I remember, however, quite a high-powered club visiting us in Belfast from America. They went to one theatre where the surgeon did a prostatectomy, on this occasion with the loss of no blood. The visitors were greatly impressed and one of them said, "Professor, whose technique do you employ?"

"Oh," said the surgeon, "I usually do Horner's operation."

"Well, Sir, that is a new name to us, we have never heard of Professor Horner."

So they took their notebooks out and got the pencils at the ready. However, when the surgeon said, "He put in his thumb and pulled out a plum, and said 'What a good boy am I,'" they were not amused. The notebooks were closed and they slipped into the theatre next door.

Debunking I am sure is a good thing at times. The story is told in Belfast of one of our surgeons at a surgical meeting telling his personal results with a new operation. He said he had now done nine cases so far by this new method. Sadly he had had two deaths. His opposite number, always glad to score a point, said that perhaps he had been more lucky in his choice of cases, as he had now done fifteen of these with just one death. For fear this nonsense was going to escalate, another surgeon from a different hospital, with a better sense of humour, said of course that he had not had the experience or the good luck of the two previous surgeons as, in fact, he had just done one case with two deaths. He then explained that the patient himself had died and at the graveside his widow had had a stroke and had died also. I do not know if the first two speakers realised what it was all about.

In 1957 a group of six British doctors received an invitation to visit Russia. This was in return for a visit by six Russian doctors who had come to Britain some months earlier. The Russians, as guests of the British Medical Association, had been entertained both medically and socially, with visits to London, Oxford, Cambridge, and Edinburgh; in fact the whole affair had been a great success and had been much appreciated.

I was honoured to be asked to be included in the return party. Our team consisted of two physicians, two surgeons, one radiotherapist, and one lady doctor. The lady doctor, Mary Esselmont, had been there before and knew to bring a vital piece of technology with her – a bath plug. It is no easy matter trying to enjoy a bath if you have to keep one heel in

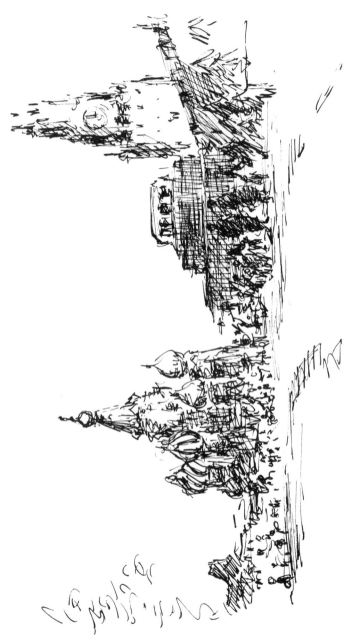

Six British doctors received an invitation to visit Russia

the plughole all the time. You need to be an expert acrobat to be able to manage it.

My colleague, and much my senior, was Sir Geoffrey Jefferson, a man I knew well and had always greatly admired. I had known him for years, and I knew one of the great man's minor failings was that time meant nothing to him. It is said that on one occasion he asked the porter at the gate of the Manchester Royal Infirmary to tell him confidentially whether it was Monday or Tuesday. The porter in great confidence said that, in fact, it was Thursday. I remember an occasion when Geoffrey came to Belfast to unveil a portrait of Cecil Calvert, a colleague of my own whose brilliant career came to a sudden end when he was killed instantly in a motor accident. On the occasion of this visit, Geoffrey Jefferson took the plane to Dublin instead of to Belfast, and finding that he was now in the wrong place he took a taxi to Belfast. I remember him arriving at my own home where we were having a small luncheon party, now long overdue, waiting for the visitor. I also remember that he had not, nor indeed had I, the necessary small change to pay the taxi. I fully understood what Lady Jefferson meant when, as we boarded the plane in London for Russia, she whispered in my ear, "Do please keep an eye on Geoff."

One evening in Moscow we were visited by our host, to make arrangements for the next day. He asked us when we would arrive, as he hoped to have four operations ready for us. Sir Geoffrey said that we would be at the hospital at 9 am. However, I saw our host to the door and told him that we would not be there until 10 am. Next day I started fussing early, but in fact we arrived at the hospital at 11 am. This was very awkward, and we did not get a very warm welcome. The reason for this was that the professor had laid on four brain cases. In the large operating theatre there were four tables, one in each corner. At 7 30 am four women surgeons had started work on each case, under local anaesthesia, preparing the bone and the skin flap to have the skull opened and the brain exposed and ready for us at 10 am. The idea was that the professor himself would then go from case to case to do the detailed intracranial operation, perhaps removing a tumour or deal with an aneurysm, or whatever the lesion was; but the delay of one hour meant that the local anaesthetic was now wearing off, and the patients were beginning to suffer considerable pain. I had great sympathy for the Russian surgeon and fully understood his annoyance. Nevertheless, the operations were carried out with great skill. Local anaesthesia makes for gentle handling of the tissues as well as the patient.

A general surgical case that I will always remember is worth recording. Caustic soda by reason of its hydroscopic properties is present on the window sills of many Russian homes. It helps to defrost and clear the windows in the cold weather. The universal availability of this dangerous fluid means that it is often taken accidentally, sometimes by children, but is also taken as a means of committing suicide. As the fluid goes down the gullet it causes permanent scarring and total and permanent blocking of the oesophagus. The only treatment is to replace the oesophagus. The case that we saw was again done entirely under local anaesthesia. After the abdomen had been opened, a large piece of the upper small intestine was freed for a distance of about 15 inches and detached at one end, still making sure that there was a good blood supply. The open end of this piece of intestine was now pushed up under and through the diaphragm then through the pleural cavity, behind the sternum to finally appear above the clavicle on the left side of the neck. To make its transit through the chest easier the patient had had the lung collapsed on that side on the previous day, by means of a pneumothorax. After the intestinal anastomosis had been tidied up, the abdomen was closed and a few days later the open end of the intestine in the neck would be joined up to the oesophagus just above the obstruction. It was a marvellous piece of surgical technique. This operation, I should say, was quite a common one at that time, as many of my other friends have told me who have visited Russia.

George Pickering, Regius professor of medicine at Oxford, was one of our party and, because of his interest in high blood pressure, we were shown some experiments. Monkeys apparently are very loyal to their spouses. They showed us one case where the male monkey in one cage was separated from his lady wife. She was put in another cage a short distance away with another male monkey and so our friend the No 1 monkey had to witness with dismay all the sexual play going on. His blood pressure rose, whose would not? They then went on to point out that if the monkeys were reunited within a certain time his blood pressure would come back to normal, but if this anxiety, frustration, and anger went on too long irreversible hypertension resulted. In all a very interesting experiment.

We did not see any animal experimentation except the monkeys and their psychological problems, but we did see the laboratory animals being taken out for a walk in the park. The Russians still carry on the Pavlov idea and insist on as little cruelty as possible; in fact they pride themselves on this, which pleased me greatly.

We were a very happy party. We had on one occasion a great discussion as to whether or not the Russian women wore corsets, and so Mary Esselmont, pretty stout herself, was asked to carry out the necessary research by banging into as many fat Russian ladies as possible. We felt it was better for her to do it than any of us. This was our only piece of research and sadly I have now forgotten the result.

# After work

Retirement affects people in different ways. Some cannot wait for their 65th birthday to arrive; in fact more and more people decide to call it a day by retiring early by one or more years. Others seem taken by surprise when the day finally arrives. The sensible person has anticipated this event by one or two years and has a programme sketched out in his mind of what he hopes to do. He has been an amateur gardener; he now becomes a professional. He was a weekend golfer; he now gets on to the links on a Monday morning, when he runs into the parsons who are relaxing after their strenuous Sundays. I remember when I retired I felt rather ashamed to be seen on the golf course during the week. I had been, I suppose, a rather manic worker. Just before retiring I did at times wish I had not to get up to be at the hospital bedside at 9 am where I knew a large class of students was waiting for me. I always very much enjoyed the ward rounds; there was such an interesting feedback from the students, but it was the necessity to be there: I *should* be there, I *must* be there, and I *ought* to be there. I suppose we must agree with Ogden Nash that the Englishman often dies from hardening of the "oughteries".

I have many happy memories of bedside teaching. I remember when I was a young registrar, a stage in life when one knows everything. I was demonstrating a case of intermittent claudication to a large class. All was going well; I pointed out that the artery closed, the blood supply was cut off to the calf muscles, the patient had to stand and wait, and to avoid embarrassment often became a window gazer, which masked his inability to walk. Eventually for good measure I said that the word came from *claudo* – the Latin "to close", and for good measure I declined it, "Claudo, clausivi, clausitum, claudere," I suppose to show off my "A" level Latin. This went down well with all the class except for one student. I was not surprised next day to get a letter from this man which went somewhat as follows: "Sir, you have undoubtedly a great knowledge of surgery, but sadly your Latin is not of the same quality. In actual fact the word claudication comes from the word *claudico* – I limp." He went on to decline this also as I had done, finally ending up by saying, "You will remember, Sir, that the Emperor Claudius was a limper." I had not forgotten it as I had never known it. In later years, I am glad to say, this young student, whose throat I probably wanted to cut at that time, became a close friend. He is today in good health, a retired and much decorated surgeon-rear-admiral.

Declining this Latin verb reminds me of the story of the young man who with two friends went to a restaurant for an evening meal. When the wine waiter came in our friend in a rather flamboyant voice asked him for a bottle of hock, and to show off his Latin he then proceeded to say "Hic, haec, hoc, you know." After 15 minutes no wine appeared and the wine waiter was called. The young man complained that the wine had not arrived. The wine waiter than said, "Yes, Sir, I heard you ordering a bottle of hock but immediately afterwards you declined it." The waiter was a young graduate with an honours degree in classics, doing a temporary job to earn an honest penny.

Some surgeons when they reach retirement age feel that they cannot give up surgery, so they continue in full time work overseas, either taking a well paid job in the oil producing countries, or a less well paid one in the Third World, perhaps even in a mission hospital. This prolongs their working life but when that stops it all ends abruptly as there is now nothing to do at home. They have cut off their home links entirely. Others keep their surgical interests going with private practice. This makes retirement a more gentle affair. The surgical patients get fewer and fewer. Finally the surgeon is left with a few old friends and supporters who are seen over and over again. In the glass and paper industry this is called recycling. Before retiring, when you saw someone and, after full examination, found he was all right you told him you could find nothing wrong and to forget all about it, but if there was a problem to come back and see you in a year or two; but when retired you say that you find things all right, and just to come and see you again in a fortnight or so.

There is the unfortunate man who cannot take retirement. He has no interests. He was a splendid surgeon, normal in every way, but he cannot face up to the vacuum. Sadly, some of these men end up, from loss of interest, with loss of memory and they become miserable in every way.

It is interesting that often the man who has not realised that 65 has come along is the very one who, when he got on to the staff of the hospital 30 years ago, immediately went through the ages of all his chiefs and knew to the day when each would retire. During the war my commanding officer every fortnight used to produce a red book called the Army List, and with a blue pencil mark certain names, gradually seeing his own slowly moving up the ladder. Many people do not realise that all their juniors have been watching their age with interest, and there are only so many rungs on the ladder. One young man who had watched this happening decided to write a letter to himself. This he deposited at the bank with the instruction that it was to be sent to him on his 64th birthday. It went something as follows: "Old man, you will be retiring in twelve months' time. Do this with grace and gratitude. If so, you will be loved and respected by your junior colleagues. SIGNED Yourself."

I have retired several times since retiring. I retired recently from the council of the Royal College of Surgeons in Ireland, on which body I had been, admittedly, for far too long. I told one senior colleague that I was going to retire; he said very kindly, "We will miss your mature judgment." I hope he meant it. On the same day I ran into a much younger man and I told him the same. His reply was, "High time," and I know he meant it.

Retirement is not an incident but rather a syndrome. You

find so many people are involved. One wife, when her husband retired, said that in her marriage vows she had married him for better, for worse, in sickness and in health, but not for lunch. The retired surgeon has a very different status in the house compared with the operating theatre. There he was, and rightly, the supremo, but in the kitchen he has no status; in fact he can be a nuisance. The pots and pans do not get, and do not need, the same sterility treatment as his operating kit. The dog has found a new master. There is a closer relationship than before. The master used to take him out for a short walk, and now the dog takes the master out for a long walk, which is very good for both. The grandchildren come into their own. He knew their number and their sex, but was not always sure he put the right name on each, nor did he know their ages. However, he is not as bad as the man in the story that is often told who was out with his wife with a long family trail behind. Suddenly the wife asked her husband, "Where is Albert?" to which he is said to have replied, "Have we an Albert?"

I have been looking at the post-retirement interests of my friends. One physician, a neurologist, cannot wait until he gets back to music. It will indeed be a change for him to tap the ivory keys rather than some scraggy old lady's knees. One surgeon tells me he is waiting for the day he can get down to painting, which will fill all his free time. Another has taken up theology. The most recently retired has taken on the presidency of the Rugby Union and hopes to travel the world in the interests of Rugby football, something that has lain dormant in his system until he retired. Others blossom as gardeners, with magnificent gardens and manicured lawns, even opening them to the public. Many just enjoy life and their family. They can do the things they have wanted to do – such as travel and read. One of my friends took up woodwork, one became a specialist in silver, a third got down to his stamp collection. Another professor is now an expert in repairing grandfather clocks. He has more friends than he had before. It does not matter what it is as long as it is something.

I once asked a very senior and busy non-academic surgeon,

with a large country and farming practice, what was the first thing he noticed on retiring. He said at once that he now paid his bills with clean notes straight from the bank. Before retiring he always had a mass of rather scruffy £10 notes that had been pushed into his hand by some country farmer. The farmer usually paid his bill handing out the notes slowly, one at a time, hoping that the surgeon would say "stop". On occasions if the surgeon did not say "stop" the farmer might give him an extra £5 note which the surgeon would give back as a "luck penny". On selling a cow in the market the farmer was accustomed to give a £5 note as a "luck penny" and, seeing his wife's operation was almost as important as the sale of one of his heifers, he felt that he should get something back from the surgeon. As you can see, there is more to surgery than standing at the side of an operating table with a scalpel in your hand.

Some retired men take up writing. If it is a highly technical subject this can raise problems, as with medical advances happening daily a work of real academic medicine needs to be written by the man in the hurly-burly of medical research. On the other hand the mature person can write a very valuable encyclopaedia or an anthology on the progress of research. Then there are others – no names, no pack drill – who just write memoirs and reminiscences. What they write, of course, reveals as much about themselves as about the people and events they describe. For most people life is a mixture of serious affairs fortunately interspersed with trivia. The average man needs the swing from work to play, from tension to relaxation. We all have these two ingredients in different amounts. It is the individual balance that makes for personality. Some people sail through life enjoying the trivia only – no use to themselves or society in general. Some, on the other hand, are obsessed with serious problems. They may become worldly successes but surely they miss much of the fun of life.

During the war with a long list of serious battle casualties we always put in a trivial case – a "tiddler" – from time to time, giving rest mentally and physically to all concerned. Even on the golf course a short hole, a bogey 3, appears every now and then to rest the golfing tiger and give the golfing rabbit a chance. One famous London surgeon always in his long and important operation list put in a case of circumcision, often just after a brain tumour. Whether this was to tease American visitors or satisfy his own ego we never knew, but I think it did both.

Mentioning a brain tumour reminds me of the occasion when that particular surgeon was operating on a patient under local anaesthesia for a brain lesion. The scalp and bony flap had been turned down and the brain surface was fully exposed. At this particular moment the patient, fully conscious, insisted on going home. No serious explanation of why he should not go would satisfy him. He was quite adamant, and the situation had reached an impasse. Suddenly the surgeon decided to move the patient and the table to the window. He pointed out to the patient that it was raining cats and dogs outside and if he went out he would get his brain wet. The patient fully understood and the operation was completed secundum artem. Dickson Wright was a man who had an answer to all questions.

Memoirs and reminiscences are unbalanced. Recently I had to put down my best-loved dog. It caused me a week of great sorrow. I did the right thing; the dog had an inoperable tumour – in fact if I had developed the same lesion I would hope that my best friend would put me down also. But in the case of the dog I felt I had let him down as I was not able to explain to him that this was for his own good. On the same day as the dog was put down there was a terrible air crash in the Far East, with the loss of 300 lives. I am afraid that that tragic incident did not affect me as much as the loss of Archie. Memoirs are unbalanced and their values can be unfair. I hope therefore that readers will treat these reminiscences of mine with indulgence, knowing them for what they are: neither a history nor a life story, but a purely personal interpretation of events.

He pointed out to the patient it was raining cats and dogs

# A last word

I said at the beginning that this was a personal saga of some of the incidents in my surgical professional life. I have tried to keep my own personal and family life out of it as far as possible because I think that matters of that sort should be one's own personal property, but I find I have mentioned family affairs on occasions, so I feel I should give the entire overall picture.

I have had one of the happiest lives that any man could wish for – a very happy home life, entirely due to my wife and our two children. I look back with much pleasure to our wedding in September 1931, and it is right that I should put on paper my gratitude for the love and support that has come my way in my home over the years since.

# Index

145

149